Texas Wine Pioneers

HOW TEXAS UPSET THE WORLD WINE STAGE AND CONTINUES TO REDEFINE IT

Gretchen Glasscock

First Edition, 2020

ISBN: 978-1-7360176-0-9 (Hardcover)
ISBN: 978-1-7360176-1-6 (Paperback)
ISBN: 978-1-7360176-2-3 (ebook)

www.advancingtexaswine.com

Editor: Barbara Noe Kennedy
Book cover design/Interior design: Asya Blue

Dedication

Deepest thanks to Leon Adams, author of *The Wines of America* and expert on wine laws in the United States, who showed us where the goalposts were; and Pike Powers, legislative powerhouse who strategized and crafted the Farm Winery Bill, then recruited the legislative team that aggressively pushed it down the field and over the line, particularly the combative and courageous Representative John Wilson, who stopped the opposition in their tracks several times; and in my own Bexar County, Representative Frank Tejeda, a loyal colleague and supportive professional friend, warm and personable and a true champion. Without these warriors and, indeed, my entire viticultural, winemaking and communications teams, there would be no historic Farm Winery Act. On behalf of all winegrowers and wine lovers in Texas, I would like to thank them all and hope they attain their rightful place in the honored annals of Texas wine history. I also would like to thank all the winegrowers who have bravely chosen this pioneering path of developing Texas wines.

"The discovery of a new vineyard does more for the happiness of mankind than the discovery of a new star."

— Jean Anthelme Brillat-Savarin
1755-1826

Table of Contents

"Looking back over 30 years, I feel that Glasscock had a strong suit and it was Vision – with a capital 'V.'"
—Vintage Texas

Introduction

This book provides new details recorded by a Texas wine pioneer, advocate, activist and entrepreneur who lived it. Working with dedicated professionals who believed, as I did, that the future of Texas wine held great promise, I was a vigorous, groundbreaking participant in challenging the first definitions of Texas grape-growing regions, planting the first commercial vinifera grape vineyard in Texas, helping form the Texas Grape Growers Association and passing the historic landmark legislation, the Farm Winery Act, HB 2229, which laid the foundation and enabled the development of a multibillion-dollar Texas wine industry.

This is a tale of epic battles and larger-than-life personalities, including iconic global winemakers, titans of the wine industry, newcomers who wanted to create this groundbreaking new industry and Texas legislators who either caved or fiercely fought the well-financed liquor lobby that had one goal: to kill change.

And we will explore the future of the Texas wine industry, particularly in this present moment of a pandemic that has forced wine-tasting rooms and wine festivals to shut down. The future necessarily will bring in a new era of online wine sales. And we will be prepared to embrace it in a way that will create new prosperity for Texas wine.

CHAPTER ONE

The Day That Rocked the World of Wine

Judgement of Paris: California vs. France and the Historic 1976 Paris Blind Tasting

The Judgement of Paris in 1976 was a moment that rocked the world of wine and set it on a different course. This was a moment, at a well-known, respected and well-publicized blind wine tasting in Paris, with French judges, that two California wines took first place over their French counterparts, proving that, given a level playing field, California and American wines could compete with the top wines in the world.

Stag's Leap Wine Cellars walked off with top honors as a California Cabernet, against top French Bordeaux wines, including Château Mouton Rothschild, Château Montrose and Château Haut-Brion. Chateau Montelena's Chardonnay, from Napa Valley, won the white wine category in a field that included some of the best and most famous French Burgundies, including the illustrious Montrachet, a Grand Cru vineyard in the Côte de Beaune.

Make no mistake: The wine industry is a competitive business. The French were shocked and did not take this upset willingly or graciously. One French judge, outraged, asked for her ballot back. But the die was cast.

American wines began to break the stranglehold French wines and, in fact,

French dining establishments had on the United States food and beverage scene. Prominent and influential celebrity chefs, such as James Beard, endorsed and promoted fresh and wholesome food and American wines, a break from the classic, dark French restaurants, with their heavy sauces and rich, classic French dishes, stars of a time when fresh food was not so bountiful and easily procured. Without denying the high quality of many of the top French restaurants and French wines, much of what they achieved has to be attributed to the success of their marketing, their aura of sophistication and their exclusivity.

What might be considered a second and many subsequent Judgement of Paris moments of awakening have now taken place, putting Texas wines at the center of a new and revised wine universe. One of the latest, the 2020 San Francisco Chronicle Wine Competition (SFCWC), received nearly 6,700 entries from over 1,000 wineries from the United States, Canada and Mexico.

Over 65 judges from a variety of fields representing various North American wine regions completed the judging on January 10, 2020, to determine the best wines in North America. Best of Class awards went to the following Texas wines:

- Brennan Vineyards – 2015 Viognier – Comanche County
- English Newsom Cellars – 2018 Roussanne – Texas High Plains
- Longhorn Cellars – Brindle Blend – Texas
- Lost Draw Cellars – 2018 Marsanne – Texas High Plains
- Messina Hof Winery – 2017 Paulo Blend – Texas
- Perissos Vineyard and Winery – 2017 Aglianico – Texas Hill Country
- Spicewood Vineyards – 2017 Tempranillo – Texas High Plains

Many more Texas wines won top honors as they have for years. There is no question, in terms of quality, Texas wines have definitely arrived. A look back will tell us how we got to this place and where we go from here.

State of Wine Tastes and Consumption in the 1970s

In the 1970s, we lived in a very different world and a very different grape-growing, wine knowledge and wine consumption culture than we do today.

In the 1970s there was no Google to help with research, no Facebook to network or share ideas, no cell phones to keep in touch. The Beatles released their final album, "Let It Be." Disney World opened in Orlando, Florida, with the price of $3.50, as opposed to today's price of $105 for a day pass for those over 10 years old. Seventies fashions featured flower power, bell bottoms, and military surplus.

Fashions in wine were dramatically different as well. Blue Nun, a sweet, white German wine, was the most popular wine in the world. Owner "[Peter] Sichel targeted the export market. Beginning in the 1950s, Blue Nun was advertised as a wine that could be drunk throughout an entire meal, thereby eliminating the often intimidating problem of wine and food pairing. Blue Nun can be said to have been the first wine to have been produced and effectively marketed with an international mass market in mind. ... The brand became spectacularly popular in the United Kingdom and the United States, selling for the same price as a second growth red Bordeaux wine. At its peak of popularity in 1984–1985, annual sales in the US were 1.25 million cases, with another 750,000 cases sold elsewhere."[1]

One reason for Blue Nun's popularity, aside from its slight sweetness, was its reliability of always offering the same tasting experience. Due to the massive volume of grapes and wine the company controlled, their winemakers always were able to pull from different sources and create the same taste, much like Coca-Cola. You knew what you were going to get. Uniformity was the goal.

---

1 https://en.wikipedia.org/wiki/Blue_Nun

Evolution of New American Cuisine - Fresh, Seasonal, Local

But times were changing. California had been an outlier. It had started humbly, as most wine regions do, many begun by Franciscan fathers who came to the New World and cultivated their own grapes. But over the years, with the diligence of some of California's pioneering wine-growing families, California wine began to slowly take its place on the high-quality culinary scene.

As someone who was attending Columbia University and living in New York City in that era, I was, like everyone else, dazzled by The Four Seasons restaurant, originally created in 1959, a design icon by Ludwig Mies van der Rohe and Philip Johnson, and a ground-breaking entry into the restaurant industry. Not only did it break with the dark and cozy French style and classic French-inspired menu of the top restaurants of the day, it went for stylish, even stark, modern decor, but with an enormous and impressive Picasso tapestry and seasonally-changing menus with much American sourced food. And it was one of the first major destination restaurants to offer American, primarily Californian, wines. It was a major breakthrough in prestige for the California wine industry. It also served to educate many connoisseurs of fine wine that classic wine grapes, grown in the right climates, can be among the best wines in the world, regardless of which state or country produced them. Even everyday wine drinkers were beginning to realize that sweetness and uniformity, like that offered by Blue Nun, might have its limitations. Far more interesting could be the subtle variations of different regions, seasons, and stylistic choice by individual winemakers, more like individual and handsewn or regional styles of blouses and clothing as opposed to mass-produced, standardized clothing. It was the variations that created interest and led to ever more exploration.

American cuisine was morphing as well, with California, once again, leading the way. Alice Waters, now a food icon, opened Chez Panisse in 1971. Her enduring principles brought to the forefront of American cuisine the concepts of freshness, seasonality and local sourcing. Whereas the innovative Four Seasons, opened in

1959, elevated the concept of seasonality, it did so by importing ingredients from wherever they were in season; they were able to execute their huge seasonal menu by importing food from England, Norway, Belgium, Oregon or wherever the desired items were fresh and in season.

Alice Waters, in California, had a different concept. Hers was very much a forerunner of farm-to-table, natural and freshly sourced. A food revolution ensued, resulting in a growing number of "locavores" eating only locally sourced food. The movement also was meant to bring about social change, protecting the environment, supporting small local farms, and providing a sustainable alternative to overprocessed corporate and industrial farming. Local sourcing and freshness were meant to bring to the forefront deeper, more authentic flavors, sustain local farmers who cared for the land, and, ultimately, provide a more fully meaningful food experience for all of us. These concepts applied to wine as well.

And, with those shifts in attitude, adventurous people in various parts of the United States began to feel empowered to explore wine-making conditions in their own regions. The wine grape, after all, did not know where it was; it only responded to the soil, climate and growing conditions around it and, ultimately, to the artistry of the winemaker who crafted it into a unique wine.

Texas' Many Hard-earned "Judgement of Paris" Moments

In 1986 Llano Estacado Winery in the High Plains of West Texas won a Double Gold award at the prestigious San Francisco Fair Wine Competition.

This was the first of many moments when Texas wine would display it had the necessary breeding and premium quality to compete on the world stage of fine wine in the United States as well as Europe.

CHAPTER TWO

Why Not Texas? And Why Not Me?

California Gave Us Insight and a Road Map

J ust as in Texas and other southwestern states, it was the Spanish Franciscan missionaries who first arrived in California to plant the mission grape and use it to make wine for communion.

The California Gold Rush in the mid-1800s brought a huge influx of miners, prospectors and dreamers into California. They prospected for gold in the day, and in the evening they created a huge demand for wine to fuel their dreams of great wealth or still the fears of failure, or merely to accompany their meals.

It was at this time that many of California's vineyards were planted and its wine centers developed.

Many families that had come to the United States from Germany and Italy were accustomed to tending to small vineyards and making table wine for their own families. Old wine families that brought that tradition to California and maintained and expanded it there included the Wentes from Germany, who still operate their winery today in Livermore, California; Secondo Guasti, who founded the Italian Vineyard Company, and Andrea Sbarboro, who established Italian Swiss Colony, both later sold to large corporations; and the Gallo brothers, who founded E. & J. Gallo Winery. By the 1900s California wines were being exported all over the world.

Just as throughout the rest of the nation, the California wine industry's progress was not only halted but decimated by Prohibition and had to be entirely rebuilt.

An initial step to help revitalize the industry was the forming of a program in Viticulture and Enology at U.C. Davis. There was also an increased focus on quality, beginning with the type of grapes that were planted. Georges de Latour and his wife, Fernande, who had come from France, founded Beaulieu Vineyard in 1900 with the goal of creating wines that could compete with the finest French wines. To that end, in 1938 Latour traveled to France and coaxed famed winemaker, André Tchelistcheff, to return with him to guide Beaulieu Vineyard. Together they set upon a program introducing vinifera grapes to the vineyards and new wine-making and aging techniques to produce the finest wines possible. André was the first great winemaker to come to the United States and put his perfectionistic imprint on wine making here. He set a standard that others still try to emulate.

In essence, California provided Texas, as well as other states, with the road map. All we had to do was follow it.

Raised as a Fourth-generation Texas Entrepreneur

Starting in the late 1950s, and particularly after the Judgement of Paris in 1976, shifts in attitude brought a new appreciation of local, original and unique tastes in both wine and food. There was starting to be less reliance on French labels and brand names and a new openness to trying California and local wines. Adventurous people across the United States were beginning to feel it might be possible to grow quality vineyards and produce premium wines in their own regions. Who would make that leap in Texas?

Why not me?

I was raised as a fourth-generation Texas entrepreneur. Although the Glasscocks were an old Texas family and there was, in fact, a Glasscock County in West Texas, the Glasscocks of my grandparents' generation were a farming family that had eventually settled near Blanco, Texas, with a modest farm and quite modest income. My father and his brothers were born around the turn of the 20th century, near Blanco in the

Hill Country, now one of the centers of the Texas wine industry. As teenagers, they started their own "circus" by painting white stripes on a donkey and using other highly imagined creatures. By their late teens, they fulfilled a lot of boys' dreams by running off to join the circus, first Ringling Brothers then Barnum & Bailey. They started out as acrobats relying on their bodies and athleticism instead of capital.

Moving up the ladder, they went into vaudeville, where the Glasscock Brothers became headliners. Once in Upstate New York, they appeared at the top of a playbill that featured Fred and Adele Astaire at the bottom. At 21, my father was Grand Marshal in a presidential parade. At an early age he had reached the top of his career.

Ultimately, vaudeville morphed and the best dressing rooms started being given to women singers and male piano players. The brothers saw the handwriting on the wall and decided to move on.

When Spindletop hit, the first big oil gusher in East Texas, the oil boom and the beginning of the oil age set off a rush to the fields, much like the Gold Rush in California had.

My father and his three brothers, by this time, were all tough, hardscrabble entrepreneurs, and now they had a new dream on their horizon. They were "poor boys" aiming to go in and succeed in a rich companies' industry led by the major oil heavyweights at the time: ExxonMobil, Shell and British Petroleum (later BP). They set out for East Texas, around Longview, and managed to lease land in the yards and playgrounds around equally poor churches and schools, out of necessity, outsmarting the big oil companies and sharing in the success that followed. They would go on to participate in almost every new oil strike in Texas during that era. My uncle, Gus, would go on to develop the first offshore oil rig in the Gulf of Mexico, leasing it to major oil companies, thus achieving some financial stability.

But there were plenty of ups and downs in the oil business. Once, when my father had hit a gusher in West Texas, he was offered $ 100,000 for it, about $1,300,000 in today's dollars. He turned it down. On his drive back home to San Antonio, the well had turned to water. He rolled with the punches. Never complain, never explain, might have been his credo. He moved on.

In the 1940s, he also started a small chain of eight theaters in little farming towns like Pleasanton, George West and Blanco. Perhaps recalling his roots in vaudeville, he opened each one with a live show, Western music with a local draw like his pal Red River Dave playing the guitar and singing Western songs. At the beginning, each theater made about $60,000 in a year, $864,000 in today's dollars. A few years later, with the major advent of television, the entire chain made about $60,000 in a year.

During this time, my father bought land in Blanco, Texas, and he also owned the entire small main city block, which included his theater and the jail. (Ultimately, he gave a large portion of that land to the Girl Scouts for their camp.)

He was also accumulating ranchland in a number of counties in South Texas.

All the Glasscock brothers were equally bold and rode into history as pioneers, first as athletes, then as entrepreneurs, then in their groundbreaking oil, gas and mineral businesses. Ultimately, they returned to their roots in the land, purchasing not farms, but ranches.

My father again pioneered by raising the new Santa Gertrudis breed of cattle, first developed by the King Ranch, bred to thrive in harsh, particularly hot climates like South Texas.

By the time I was born in the forties, my father was in his mid-fifties, and we were his second generation of children. The first, a brother and sister who were a generation older than me, had been through all the harrowing hard times and ups and downs of my father's tough climb to success. Consequently, they were both extremely risk-averse and, as you might imagine, did not reflect my father's values or his vision for the family future.

I, on the other hand, as well as my brother and sister, were born after my father and mother were comfortably off and the occasional hard times of the businesses we experienced did not affect our quality of life. The future my mother saw for us was to be well educated and refined, knowledgeable about the finer things. What my father saw was potential entrepreneurs, pliable and ready to be shaped in his entrepreneurial mold.

My father had great admiration for my mother, who had supported the family teaching school during the Depression. He believed, unlike most men of his time, that women were extremely smart and capable of achieving any goals they set. Possibly because of this mindset, at some point, he settled on me to learn the family business. He spent a lot of time teaching me. I think he spent time, initially, with my sister and brother as well, but for whatever reason, that ground did not seem as fertile to him.

I remember when I was about 10 years old, my father took me out and pointed to a building. "How much is that building worth?" he asked. The correct answer was, "As much as you can get for it." And he told me about some harrowing hard times along the road to success. Once, when he was a tightrope walker in the Glasscock Brothers circus act, during a particularly rough winter in Upstate New York, he got down to his last quarter. In a, no doubt, untypical response, he was disgusted and pitched his last quarter over a roof. He then borrowed some money, had some circus tickets printed, took a train to the next town and sold them, came back and put his own circus together. He then took the circus back to the town where he had sold the tickets. He was back in business. The lesson was clear to me: You had to take risks. If you had fear, you had to manage it. And, most important, you had to keep ahead of the curve of change in business so it didn't wash over you.

He also spent a lot of time teaching me to play poker, which he said was the businessman's game. It is a fact that one can deal out a thousand hands to four players and each would receive about the same number of winning hands. The key was how you bet on them. Run up the pot when you had a winning hand; fold when you didn't. He also occasionally cheated because he said you had to learn to look out for people cheating. Eventually I became very expert in poker.

Since I was raised from the perspective and expectation of being an entrepreneur, ultimately, I would be expected to run the family's businesses. Shortly before 1970, after my father passed, I returned to San Antonio from Columbia University in New York City, where I had lived for a number of years, getting my bachelor's degree in writing. The job I inherited was to manage my family's 20,000 acres of ranchland and mineral interests in South Texas. Despite accompanying my father to our ranches, learning to ride and even shoot, I was still very much a city girl, accustomed to searching out museums and art galleries, reading classic literature. T.S. Eliot and Camus were favorites at the time. I couldn't compete with some women who had basically been born and bred on ranches and found it a more native environment, well suited to their temperament and skill set.

Generally, I was compared to our next-door neighbor, rancher Mary Nan "Pet" West of the famously flamboyant "Silver Dollar" Jim West clan (which included Sandra West, who requested and was buried in her blue Ferrari). Pet, who became a different generation friend and unattainable role model, had 40,000 acres next to our ranch in Zavala County. She could ride and rope, shoot and curse as well as or better than any ranch hand around. She also had breathtaking emerald and diamond jewels she showed off with elegant gowns on formal occasions. I was no Pet West, to put it mildly. But my father had been bringing me to ranches as soon as I was old enough to walk. So I knew my way around our ranches, had some good boots and wasn't afraid of either riding or hard work. At the time I wore a pistol and kept close by a .22 rifle and a Browning Sweet Sixteen shotgun to ward off snakes, wild Javelina hogs and other varmints. Also, since I was frequently surrounded by groups of 25 or so cowboys, I occasionally pulled out my pistol and shot a beer can off a fence, just to demonstrate my self-protection skills. Shooting and poker were at the top of my father's curriculum for me, so I had mastered both.

I began overseeing our ranches, with the help and guidance of our long-time foreman, Ed Bludeau.

Looking for Dramamine to Inject into a Bumpy Ride

By then, I already was familiar with the roller-coaster, rags-to-riches-and-back-again ride of the oil and gas industry, a true volatile commodity business. I understood I had been tapped to work, not just for me, but for my mother and family, so I tried to use my education, and a natural love of and affinity for research, to figure out how to inject a little dramamine into the inevitably bumpy ride. I set out to learn how to make the most of our ranching agribusiness, which, unfortunately, was not only another commodity business, but, being dependent on nature and subject to droughts, could also be a bumpy ride.

CHAPTER THREE

Texas Conditions – Can We Do This?

Exploring Texas Wine Conditions -
Texas A & M Takes a Shot

As in most agribusiness operations, one is sitting on a lot of land relative to the revenue you are able to generate off of it. As it turns out, I shared this conundrum with the University of Texas and Texas A & M, which jointly owned about 2 million acres in West Texas and whose profits were put in the Permanent University Fund. In fact, I was told at the time that if that land wasn't undervalued on the books, the university system would surpass even Harvard in wealth.

As it also turns out, there is a line that goes down West Texas: On one side is oil, and on the other side, tumbleweed. Fortunately, the University of Texas lands were on the oil side and derived significant revenue from their oil and gas holdings. The UT regents, however, along with land surface manager, Billy Carr, wanted to address how to generate more money from their land surface, and also how to generate revenue when the oil eventually ran out.

To this end, they assigned Texas A & M to conduct a grape feasibility study led by horticulture professors Ronald Perry and Hollis Bowman. It seemed clear to me and, I think to many others, that California could serve as a template for the development of a Texas wine industry. One could look back and see nonproductive land turned into plentiful orchards and vineyards through the right growing conditions, varietal selection and careful husbandry of the land. Since California's grape vineyards stretched from the cool North Coast, with its premium wine grape conditions, to the blistering heat of the Central Valley, with its huge production of wine grapes of "everyday" or jug wine quality, one of the immediate questions the study would hope to answer is, "What quality of wine grape would Texas be capable of growing?" In other words, what would be the economic impact of vineyard development and wine production of premium wine at high prices versus everyday table wines that families might consume more often and possibly make up revenue by the greater quantity produced (with Gallo as an example)? Either way, or with both, the creation of a serious, commercial wine industry in Texas would be an economic boon for the state, and, in time, could be a substantial source of additional income for farmers or those interested in pursuing agribusiness.

An initial version of the study showed that, yes, most regions of Texas could grow wine grapes, but they all were designated a Region V, or, as hot as California's Central Valley, which only had the capability of growing ordinary or table or jug wine. To clarify, in 1980, the process of establishing a well-delineated American Viticultural Area, or AVA, was initiated, and specific areas began to be officially designated as an AVA. At that point it became clear that Texas had eight clearly identified AVA regions with different climates and growing characteristics.

In the 1970s, however, there was no such designation and no areas that had been specifically researched for their viticultural characteristics. A potential grape grower was left pretty much on his or her own to figure out the most promising areas. Region V was not promising for producing high-quality wines, particularly ones that could compete with France or California wines produced in the cooler Regions II or III.

Ron Perry and Hollis Bowman used in their study the "degree days" formulation to evaluate a region's potential for grape growing. Climactic regions for grapes are "based on the summation of heat as degree-days above 50 degrees Fahrenheit for the period from April 1 to October 31. Grape-producing regions will fit into one of these categories," as outlined in *Grape Growing* by Robert J. Weaver and many other technical books:

> I. Cool regions - less than 2,500 degree-days of heat. This would be comparable to Germany where it is very cool but sunshiny during the day. This allows the grapes to rest at night and develop a lot of complex flavors that you can taste on your tongue.

II. Moderately cool regions – 2,501 to 3,000 degree-days of heat, like Napa, Northern Californian and parts of France.

III. Warm regions – 3,001 to 3,500 degree=days. This would be comparable to parts of France and California, like Paso Robles and St. Helena.

IV. Moderately hot regions – 3,501 to 4,000 degree-days. Modesto, California, where Gallo is located, and the nearby Central Valley region of Stockton are two examples.

V. Hot regions - more than 4,000 degree-days. Fresno and Bakersfield, both in California, fill this niche and are suitable for jug wines.

Grapes located in Region IV or V, the warmer regions, don't enjoy the cooler temperatures at night required to allow them to rest and, therefore, they don't develop complex flavors. Instead, the grapes have a flat, uniform taste, which is not a bad thing, if that's your goal. Jug wines by Gallo, for example, are ordinary table wines of good but uniform quality; somewhat like Coca-Cola, it's a taste you can count on. (Many of us remember when Coca-Cola tried to introduce a slightly different flavor, branded "New Coke." Despite prior research indicating the public might like the slightly sweeter flavor, the new formulation was a dismal failure with consumers and, within three months, "New Coke" was ditched, the original formulation was returned and henceforth known as "Coca-Cola Classic." So, uniformity definitely has a value.)

One has to accept the fact that climate is one thing that a vintner cannot change (although Nature may change it over time and, in another context, some advocates are trying to impact climate change). Even soil, which is an important variable, can be altered through nutrients or other ingredients added to it. The winemaker's methods can be changed or improved through technical advances in enology, vinification or aging processes. The "concept" of how a certain brand of wine should taste can remain the same through the centuries, if successful, or altered if desired. But climate is, as far as an individual vintner's efforts are concerned, a constant.

At this point in the Texas A & M study, the accepted wisdom was that Texas was capable of producing only "everyday" table and dessert wines, but lacked the necessary coolness to produce premium wines.

This classification was not a death blow, but it was not the best news either. One reason for this concerns one's ability to market the wine you make. Just as a fashion designer's label on high-priced Paris couture supports his or her ability to sell lower priced clothing through mass market or big box stores, a winery that is recognized or has received awards for its high-priced vintage or aged wines establishes its brand and finds a readier market for its affordable "everyday" wines.

Ideally, when studied in detail, Texas would have pockets of climate and soil capable of producing premium wines that could earn "bragging rights," medals, media attention and a place on the table of true wine buffs. Logically, one had to wonder if Texas really was that uniform in its climate, which, granted, only took in the growing season. It might be quite different if weather extremes throughout the year were taken into account.

Challenging Accepted Climate Wisdom

I was not the most obvious choice for someone to explore Texas wine-growing climates. I had, after all, only recently returned from New York City, where I attended writing groups at Columbia University and frequented the Broadway theater. My friends were Greek sculptors, Broadway set designers and TV actors. My roommate, Kathy Leake, an attractive and talented young woman, starred in "Little Mary Sunshine" off Broadway. I was heavily into the arts.

On the other hand, I was settling in to run a number of ranches and get to know agribusiness firsthand; I really enjoyed research, had a fierce determination when it came to business and failed to see anything completely foolhardy about taking up research that might contradict a study by Texas A & M, backed by the University of Texas. Whatever the facts were, I just wanted to take a look at them myself before accepting them as written in stone. Plus which, as a wine aficionada, I came to view wine making itself as a fusion of art and agriculture.

Armed with the current results of the Texas A & M study, I decided to explore on my own the full possibilities of potential wine regions in Texas. I had a lot to learn and set out to learn it.

My first stop was the oldest winery in Texas, dating back to 1833 (with time out for Prohibition), the Qualia family's Val Verde Winery in Del Rio. At this time, they were growing the Herbemont and Black Lenoir varieties of Black Spanish grapes, which are disease resistant and do well in this very hot climate. There, I met with third-generation vintner Thomas Qualia, an attractive and engaging fellow, steeped in wine knowledge and lore and very generous in sharing his thoughts and opinions on both wine and the Texas climate.

"I don't believe all of Texas is a Region V," he stated with conviction.

"Really?" I said. "Why is that?"

"Have you ever been to West Texas, to the Davis Mountains?"

"No."

"Well, there are pine trees and snow on the mountains, and the cattle grow thicker hide because of the climate. It is definitely not a Region V."

To me, this information was a little like the clouds parting and a ray of light shining through. It indicated that Texas might hold a region capable of producing premium wines.

"In fact," Tommy continued, "there are something like seven different regions in Texas, and I'm pretty sure they aren't all a Region V."

That, if true, was really good news, and it's all I needed to set my course for further research.

I should add that not only did Tommy Qualia's shared information ultimately change the arc of my life, but I believe the further development of the Texas wine industry changed his as well. At that time, the Val Verde Winery was producing several wines, dry and sweet amber and dry and sweet red, which sold out each year, and were passable, but definitely were not giving Napa vintners any sleepless nights. Today, with new wine knowledge and methods, the Qualias are producing many fine wines, accepting the influence of their hot climate, particularly the multiple award-winning Don Luis Tawny Port. The Val Verde Winery has now completed more than 180 years of wine making and, in my view, stands as an inspiration to Texas winemakers.

I met with several other Texas wine activists, some of whom were planning experimental vineyard plantings to determine which grapes might grow well in their regions. Among them was Clint McPherson, widely known as Doc, who had witnessed a grape spring up in his patio and dubbed it the "Patio Grape." Doc was a Texas Tech professor in Lubbock, in the High Plains area. He and two professors, Roy Mitchell, a chemist, and Dr. Robert Reed, had planted wine grapes on the university campus in 1965, and in 1971 would plant an experimental seven-acre plot with a hundred other grape varieties. The High Plains area, with sunny days and cool nights, seemed an ideal growing climate, with only the negatives of winter freezes and arid conditions that require irrigation for a crop. The wind, which blows almost constantly, does help limit any moisture that can lead to mildew or fungal disease. On balance, the climate factors were positive.

Determining to take a closer look at the Davis Mountains area, the High Plains and the Texas wine region study itself, I began my research in earnest.

Mentoring – The Infusion of Hard-won Experience

At this time, as a family ranch owner-manager, I was getting some advice and mentoring from B. K. (Belton Kleberg) Johnson's group, particularly Dudley Campbell, who served as the group's president, at their office based in San Antonio. There they maintained a staff with various experts, with retired military colonels acting as assistants and drivers (to give one an idea of the level of training, expertise and discipline they required in order to serve in that office).

Many South Texas ranching families set up offices, and sometimes homes, in San Antonio. Some of them maintained suites, much like homes, in the grand and historic St. Anthony hotel.

Dudley was an amiable and empathetic gentleman, a longtime South Texas rancher and farmer with a Bachelor of Science from Texas A & I University and Master of Science from Colorado State University. B. K., known as "B," was a Kleberg and one of the heirs to the 825,000-acre King Ranch in Kingsville, Texas, as well as owner of the Chaparrosa Ranch, about 100 miles southwest of San Antonio. He also owned properties in other countries and served on the boards or had associations with many global organizations including A & T. This gave "B" and Dudley and their staff a deep and extensive knowledge, not only of the nuts and bolts of running businesses but many of the nuances and subtleties that can come into play, particularly in areas where one is not a native.

At the same time, I was also dealing with, or being mentored by, some of San Antonio's top lawyers who were sorting out matters in my father's estate. As it turned out, one of his first-generation children did not take well to our father splitting his estate among us. Ideally, he wanted it all, or at least the lion's share, so he began suing my mother, sister, brother and me regularly, making it really unavoidable that we hire lawyers to respond to his lawsuits and ultimately resolve these various issues. Although expensive, this turned out to be a blessing in some respects. For five years, I dealt most days with a real estate lawyer and a tax lawyer—meaning, later on, when those issues had been long resolved, I was, for a layperson, pretty well versed in those areas of law, always a help in starting or running a business.

I knew enough to run our ranches with the help of our longtime foreman, particularly as I always had been very keen on research, so I continued to learn. Between my father's constant business education of me over the years, the established operating procedures, input of the foreman, fresh advice from Dudley Campbell and what I could learn myself, the ranches continued to hum along, bringing in a big part of a living for me, my mother and family. Running an established business, particularly a successful business, was relatively easy ... just keep doing what the business has always done. It did not present the steep challenges and learning curve of a start-up. And, if successful, it was self-financing. Still, there was a lot I didn't know, particularly about the dynamics involved among ranchers and the generally small-town Texas communities they operated in. Luckily for me, many very old, established ranching families at that time were very solicitous to widows and daughters of ranchers who, with limited knowledge, had to take over their husband's or father's ranching operations. In this single aspect, they seemed to set aside a generally machismo attitude toward women and view these working women like daughters or, at least, nieces who just needed a word or two of insightful, diplomatic advice to complete their ranching missions. It cannot be overstated how crucial mentoring is to gain a foothold and move up in any field, particularly a male-dominated field where women, generally, are not mentored. Even though, viewed in a rear-view mirror, this may seem a little paternalistic, it was nevertheless invaluable, and I was grateful for the advice and guidance I received.

Clearly, there were a number of occasions in which the B. K. Johnson group and Dudley, in particular, felt I needed a word or two of advice. They were not sold on the idea of vineyards, as they made abundantly clear. With just the stroke of a pen, they could arrange deals for me with major farmers who could raise corn or sorghum on my land, pay me and my family a percent of the revenue and I could be out shopping or having lunch with the other ladies. That suggestion, although no doubt economically solid, didn't make the earth move for me; it didn't appeal. Perhaps I had spent too long on the East Coast to be excited by raising corn or sorghum. However, I loved the challenge of tackling a new frontier in Texas, the possible development of a wine industry or, at least, the development of a small vineyard.

Since I was determined to explore the West Texas region, they explained the unfamiliar-to-me concept of "insiders and outsiders." According to this world view, every area has "insiders" and "outsiders." To my surprise, they considered themselves "outsiders" in a number of places where they did business: the Chaparrosa Ranch, for example. In their view, La Raza Unida, a Mexican-American group that had taken over local government, were the "insiders." So they proceeded, quite deliberately, to create collaborative alliances with that group so they, too, could have a say in local politics and the development and passage of laws at the state level.

As they explained to me, there were a number of older ranching families that owned land in West Texas, in the hundreds of thousands of acres, and I would be well served if I made a courtesy call on them before inserting myself into "their neck of the woods." They didn't actually spell out the point that things could go very badly for me if I didn't do this … not just with land barons, but with some local cowboys or "drugstore cowboys" (faux cowboys in Western garb but little ranching experience) as well, a hard fact that I would run into later. The general impression I took away was that I might not be able to buy a loaf of bread in a particular town, much less have any say over their agriculture or farm development, if I didn't have the right allies.

Okay, I got it. With that, they pointed out the Gage Ranch, an approximately 200,000-acre spread owned by the influential, sophisticated and very civic-minded Gage, Catto and Negley family, which included patrician Henry Catto, who later served as Ambassador to Britain; and, particularly, Roxanna Donnell, who had planted a seven-acre, experimental vinifera vineyard on her land, to see how it did: a good omen. I made an appointment to meet with Roxanna, and we hit it off and became friends. She was always supportive and gave good advice. She, however, was not as sanguine as I was about developing a vineyard or wine business. Roxanna pointed out that it would take three to five years for the plantings to produce grapes to make wine, and that was a long time to be pouring money into a project. She was, of course, correct. And it was entirely possible I would be biting off more than I could chew. Although technically very wealthy, Roxanna Donnell came from a different point of view than I did. Many of these old, generational mega-land owners had the perspective that they were caretakers of their land, and the most important job they had in life was to pass that land on to the next generation. Sometimes the net effect of that thinking is to become "land poor." In other words, having more land than money, although you could, in no sense of the word, be considered anything other than affluent and, actually, a multimillionaire—at least on paper.

My background, viewpoint and upbringing were quite different.

For good or ill, I was raised from the perspective of being an entrepreneur: Don't be afraid to take a gamble—it's not about the cards you are dealt but how you place your bets. If you feel strongly enough, put all your chips in; if you lose, start over. (Of course, as one gets older, one loses a little pluckiness because there is less time to rebound after a financial misstep.) My father had done it many times and always came out on the other side with more money and success than before. In comparison with Roxanna Donnell, one could say, I either had more vision or less common sense. Very likely the latter. In any case, I charged ahead.

When I first saw the Davis Mountains in West Texas, I fell in love with the place, its cool shadows that changed its look throughout the day and its distinctive beauty. South Texas, where our ranches were, was scorching hot, filled with thick, tangled mesquite shrubs and red clay dirt, which, when it rained, became much like red clay cement, clinging to your boots and possibly pulling down your trousers, as you tried to step through it. In the Davis Mountains, the air was crisp and cool and even cooler on the mountain slopes. I was in agreement with Tommy Qualia that this could not possibly be a Region V, the hottest degree-day region. So how did it come to be labeled that way?

I decided to dig a little deeper into the Texas A & M climate study. I found that the temperature reading for this region was from an instrument at the tiny Marfa airport, 20 miles away and in an entirely different degree-day region. I decided to start over and do my own climate study.

Actually, classifying the degree-days of a particular region is not rocket science. All that is required is putting out weather sensing and recording instruments in areas that are truly in the region and examining historical weather records.

I started by installing a small weather station, enclosed in a protective wooden cabinet, on the southeastern slope of Blue Mountain. I also began to collect hand-recorded weather records, dating back at least a hundred years, from local farmers and ranchers who were very happy to share them. In an age before TV, in a small, rural town that still did not have cable or virtually any of the entertainment or distraction venues we sometimes think of, weather was a critical part of each day, determining work and planting schedules, and sometimes serving as an early indicator of the success of a crop. Weather records were important; they often filled lunch or dinnertime discussions. Sharing them was an act of pride and affirmation of their importance.

By that time, I already had begun visiting and staying in touch with professors who were eyeing vineyard and eventual wine production near Fort Stockton on land owned by an endowment benefiting both the University of Texas and Texas A & M. The Permanent University Fund (PUF) included both the surface and mineral rights across 2.1 million acres and 19 counties in West Texas. It is managed by University Lands (UL) and, due to massive oil revenue at the time, funded by a budget the rest of us could only dream of. The favored mode of transportation for those from the University of Texas who visited, including the regents, was by helicopter. All equipment was first rate, state of the art and very expensive. I also began visiting with Billy Carr, who was the manager of surface interests for all 2.1 million acres of University Lands in West Texas.

He was always gracious and very helpful in sharing all viticultural information available at that time. Later he would write to me: "People with your foresight and vision on the function of West Texas lands are very stimulating and refreshing to me."

Knowing I was studying the West Texas climate—and, I think, aware that if it was proven to be cooler than a Region V and capable of growing premium wine grapes, which would increase the value of UT land as well—Billy Carr offered to loan me their thermal satellite scans. They were kept in a secure location near Blue Mountain at McDonald Observatory, owned by the University of Texas. McDonald Observatory, because it is in such a remote, underpopulated region, has little "light pollution," therefore some of the darkest skies and largest telescopes in the world to observe them. At the time, the thermal scans were a big deal and not a readily available technology. They allowed the pinpointing of cooler land surfaces and underground water on thermal maps. The availability of water, too, would come to play a critical role in the development of the wine industry in water-scarce West Texas.

One of the reasons I set to write this history was to correct some myths and misinformation that had grown up around the birth of the wine business in

Texas. One wine blog, at the time, praising my vineyard project, pegged my budget as $7 million. Not remotely close. Several zeros off. And every dollar I scraped up somewhere. There was no trust fund. I did have assets, and if I wanted capital, I needed to put those assets to good use, in order to leverage what I had and develop the capital for the vineyard and wine project. Another such myth is found on the website of a winery near the base of Blue Mountain. It states: "In 1971 Gretchen Glasscock, an oil and gas heiress, had hired NASA to determine the best place to grow grapes in Texas. The southern slope of Blue Mountain was their answer, and the Blue Mountain Vineyard was planted there in 1971."[2] It was news to me that a private individual could hire NASA for a business project. I totally agree that the Blue Mountain area, which I identified as having climate conditions similar to Napa and parts of France, is a great region to grow premium grapes. I have to note, however, that my access to the thermal scans was the result of a gracious collaboration with the university researchers. My description as an "oil heiress" might fit Mary Nan West or some others, but was not remotely true of me, at least, not in any grandiose sense. Yes, I had inherited some oil and gas property, for which I was grateful. But there were five siblings, including me, plus my mother, who retained a life estate in all the oil and gas interests during her lifetime and she was very much alive during this time. Yes, I was fortunate to come from an affluent family and I did have ranchland I could leverage. Being my father's daughter, I was bolder in my business bets than some, and that might have cast a certain aura of great wealth in the minds of some. It could just as easily have cast a suspicion of insufficient caution in the minds of others. But was I a Mary Nan West? Unfortunately, no. I was no oil heiress on the scale of Caroline Rose Hunt, daughter of wildcatter H. L. Hunt, or Randa Duncan Williams, daughter of Dan Duncan, oil and gas pipeline magnate, both multibillionaires, or even Mary Nan "Pet" West, a mere multimillionaire, perhaps halfway to a billion.

Author Leon Adams probably had something to do with that oil heiress label, since, searching for more interesting hooks when he was researching the new Texas wine scene for his book, *The Wines of America*, he kept asking me, "Does anyone ever refer to you as an 'oil princess' or 'grape princess'? Despite my repeatedly telling him "No," I think the "grape princess" moniker did make it into print a time or two.

---

2 https://chateauwright.com/about/

Discovery – New Wine Region

In the end, I would establish that the Davis Mountains area has a climate Region of II or III, the same as Napa Valley or parts of France. In Napa, California, the mean temperature in growing season is 60 to 70 degrees Fahrenheit. At the base of Blue Mountain in the Davis Mountains, the mean temperature is the same: an average day temperature of 75 degrees in growing season and an average night temperature of 55 degrees.

Now our hopes were realized, at least the first phase of them: the climate condition was suitable for a vinifera vineyard. Texas did, indeed, have at least one premium wine-growing region. If we were diligent and continued using meticulous methods, along with our boundless enthusiasm and ambition, we could grow grapes and produce wine that could compete with the finest in the world.

CHAPTER FOUR

Forming A Team – Reaching Out for Expertise

Texas Wine Activists

By the early 1970s, I was far from the only one conducting research and hoping to be part of the establishment of a groundbreaking Texas vineyard and wine industry.

Dr. Bobby Smith, a tall, personable fellow devoted to fine wines, active in numerous wine circles including in California and always ready to share his knowledge, opened a vineyard in Springtown, northwest of Fort Worth.

In Austin, Ed Auler, a lawyer who had a family ranch in the Hill Country, planted a test vineyard with the help of Texas A & M and Texas Tech, which had joined forces to work on viticultural and wine-making development. He would go on to establish Fall Creek Vineyards. He and his wife, Susan, were the kind of attractive, friendly, well-connected couple that one could imagine having access to an upscale, wine-loving audience and burnishing the image of Texas wine.

As noted previously, several professors had taken the lead with vineyard experimentation. Clinton "Doc" McPherson, with Professors Roy Mitchell and Dr. Robert Reed, out of Lubbock, were one such group.

Many others, some of whom had established small test vineyards, including Paul Vincent and Merrill Bonarrigo in East Texas, were interested in learning more about and promoting Texas vineyards. I did not meet them at the time, however, as I was primarily collaborating with professors and hopeful vintners in West and Central Texas. However, they would come to be leaders and a visionary, dominant force in the Texas wine industry.

To one degree or another, these and many more would become the Texas wine activists, all of whom contributed some measure of skill, information, experience, encouragement or enthusiasm to our overall eventual success.

What I began to realize, however, primarily through my own lack of specific, detailed and technical knowledge, was that, although some of us were serious wine buffs and loved the exploration of wine, we were all rank amateurs lacking in skills on the level it would take to move this industry forward. At that time, in my judgement, we definitely needed to introduce some serious professionalism and professional standards into our endeavors.

Leon Adams – Game Changer

Luckily for the state of wine making in Texas, primitive as it was at the time, the author of *The Wines of America* was headed to our state to survey the current state of wine making.

Leon D. Adams of Sausalito, California, was a globally recognized expert on wine, having founded the Wine Institute and the Wine Advisory Board and, to me most importantly, written several editions of *The Wines of America*. This wine bible, as described on its back cover, was "a monumental work [which] is probably the most praised and quoted wine book ever published in this country, hailed by the *New York Times* in 1973 as 'the definitive history of American wines...and exhaustive compendium that spans 400 years of domestic viticulture.'"

Not only was Adams's book critical to wine knowledge because it examined wine-making practices and progress in every wine-growing nook and cranny in America, but also because it documented how new advances in wine research and technology were enabling "everyday" wines to take their place on the

American table.

Also, Adams's view of wine happened to coincide with mine. I felt too many potential consumers were kept away from wine by "wine intimidation," fear of ordering the "wrong wine," revealing they did not know enough about wine to order the absolutely "right" wine. I felt that hesitancy had to be overcome with wine education and instilling the belief that whatever wine you happened to like, was the right wine for you. I believed moving up the ladder of wine discrimination could come later, if desired. Usually it was a process, which some undertook and others did not. But first, one had to love and enjoy wines in order to even want to begin that journey. If one felt that ordering wine was going to be an intimidating and anxiety provoking experience, that journey might never begin. One of my goals, then, was to remove the intimidation factor from one's wine selection experience.

Leon Adams, in his book *The Wines of America*, says: "I perceive a trend away from label-drinking wine snobbery toward daily use of the young, appealingly palatable, healthful wines ... I call '*everyday*' wines. They are the most important wines in any country. They cost less than milk to produce and are priced to fit within the family budget for everyday meals. Costlier vintages, priced like works of art [which many are], are bought only for special occasions; I call them Sunday wines. Importer Peter M. F. Sichel expresses the importance of everyday wines when he says: 'Wine belongs on the table, not on a pedestal.' ... Today wine is being recognized as an integral wholesome new part of the national diet. After four centuries during which Americans dined without wine, it is finally here to stay."[3] Amen to that.

When Adams headed into Texas to update his book with a new edition, reporting on the latest developments in wine production and the new and buzzing Texas wine scene, I was asked to "escort" him or act as a type of guide throughout his stay. He did not stay at my home but at the historic St. Anthony hotel in San Antonio. Other than that, I was with him morning, noon and night, showing him what was new, sharing wine with him and learning his take on it. I knew right away that his knowledge was invaluable, and not just about wine growing, techniques and quality.

In Texas, at that time, we basically had no infrastructure to support a wine

---

3 Leon Adams, *The Wines of America*, 2nd Edition (New York, McGraw Hill, 1978), xi.

industry. What we lacked were suppliers of cuttings, nutrients, academic programs, viticulturists, enologists and trained laborers to tend to the vines, as well as banks that knew how to loan to vineyards and finance wineries. In short, everything. And one of our biggest lacks was the legislation needed to support a wine industry and ensure the conditions for vineyards and wineries to prosper.

In Leon Adams, we found someone who was thoroughly familiar with the patchwork of antiquated and, in many cases, bizarre and unreasonable wine laws, and how to overcome them with new legislation … not that new wine legislation wasn't a very high bar, considering the various groups that could and would line up against it. But Adams could show us the goalposts and explain how to get there.

This was another game changer.

Equally critical, Adams knew who the best viticulturists and enologists were, knew them on a first-name basis and could pick up the phone and talk with them. Also, as it turned out, he could beseech them to take on new clients. I believed we needed this injection of professionalism and that it could save us many years of endless vineyard "experimentation" before we ever got to the realization that we did not have the appropriate wine laws that would allow the industry to continue to grow and thrive.

Viticultural and Enological Experts

The first wine industry figure Leon Adams put me in touch with was André Tchelistcheff, the first great winemaker to come to the United States from France. He encouraged Beaulieu Vineyard in California's Napa Valley to put in classic vinifera grapes, a move that created the premier vineyard of the time. He also demonstrated new wine-making techniques to them that resulted in some of the finest wines produced in the United States.

According to an article that appeared in *The Wine Stalker* in 2017, André was the "most influential winemaker of modern history. … André was born in Russia, trained in France, lifted California to greatness, and took off Washington State's training wheels." It could be said that André and his son Dimitri took the first steps to doing the same for the fledgling Texas wine industry.

At Leon Adams's urging, André came to Texas to meet with me and see for himself just what was going on with Texas' new, uncharted wine industry. One might well ask, "What was such a distinguished winemaker doing coming to such an unproven wine region?" My experience was that André was not alone in being fascinated by the chimera of a new wine region in the world. I believe he was intrigued by the challenge. He wanted to see for himself what the potential might be and perhaps wanted the further recognition of being the first on the ground, a truly influential voice in establishing a new wine region. Perhaps more fundamental, I think that he, like many involved in fine wine production, saw himself as an ambassador and missionary, hoping to spread the enjoyment of wine and the integration of it into daily life into all corners of the globe.

By the time I met André, he was about 76 years old but hyperenergetic, charming, with a big smile, twinkling eyes and a boundless enthusiasm for creating quality wines. When we traveled to vineyard sites in Texas, including mine, if someone asked if he wanted to take a break or rest, André would answer: "I can rest for 500 years when I'm dead." Okay. That answer was probably one of the keys to the reputation he had established, and left the rest of us scrambling to keep up with him.

When Leon, André and I sat down to discuss the future of Texas wines, Leon said, as he often would, "Gretchen wants to produce wines that can compete with Napa's wines." André, having visited Blue Mountain and studied our Blue Mountain climate data and soil conditions, said: "With solid methods and good guidance, I think that's perfectly possible."

Then he gave me some no doubt hard-earned advice from his distinguished and lifelong experience:

"The first concern with creating the quality of the wine, is the quality of the grape. You have the distinct advantage of being able to grow vinifera, the classic European wine grape which is proven and both experienced viticulturists and wine makers understand how to manage these grapes to make fine wine.

"As long as you just have the vineyard, however, your vines and grapes are exposed to the elements, early frosts, hail, soil diseases. They must make it past the growing season and safely into the winery.

"Once you have your own winery, you are out of peril, at least from the elements.

And, although they won't have the same cachet as estate-grown grapes, you can always purchase grapes to make wine and continue with your business."

He followed this with what I thought was a rather surprising piece of advice from someone who had built his life and reputation in the wine business:

"Wineries are like yachts. It's better to have a friend who owns one."

Eventually, I came to understand the full ramifications of the expenses of building, equipping and operating a winery. It is not for the fainthearted.

I listened and took everything André said to heart. Just as Houston oil men send their sons to look after their interests in the outback of Midland, just as many other industry leaders do, André suggested bringing on his grown son, Dimitri, also a distinguished winemaker, to be more involved with day-to-day consultation and decision-making at this phase of my vineyard planning.

Dimitri, diminutive, charming and cosmopolitan like his father, arrived with great good cheer and bonhomie in West Texas and, upon introduction, presented me with a slender gold necklace, from which hung a small but real cluster of grapes coated in gold. Who could fail to be charmed by that and consider it a good omen for our future collaboration?

So now we had two leading authorities in vineyards and wine production to guide our efforts and share our growing pool of knowledge with our university professors and Texas wine activist collaborators. We were on our way.

Planting - Water, Soil and Classic Grapes

This was when the rubber met the road: actually planting the vineyard itself. Although there were half a dozen and possibly more small, experimental vineyards, with dozens, if not hundreds of grape varieties, including vinifera, planted to see how they would grow, Glasscock Vineyards at Blue Mountain would be the first commercial vinifera vineyard planted in Texas. I had sold some ranchland in order to invest in the purchase of the Blue Mountain property, 6 miles to the southeast of historic Fort Davis on Highway 166.

Dimitri Tchelistcheff, who was guiding my vineyard development, had suggested bringing in John Moramarco of California's Callaway Vineyard as vineyard manager and his son, Jon, as resident vineyard manager. We all huddled to make the decisions that would go into establishing this first commercial vinifera vineyard in Texas.

- Blue Mountain elevation: 7,330 ft (second highest in Texas)
- Vineyard elevation: 5,500 ft, a little over a mile high
- Exposure: Southeastern slope of the mountain

Original vineyard planted: 42 acres, 18,000 vines as follows:
- 1 1/2 acres test block, 9 rows
- 3 acres Merlot, 14 rows
- 10 acres Chenin Blanc, 45 rows
- 10 acres Sauvignon Blanc, 45 rows
- 7 acres Cabernet Sauvignon Black, 32 rows

This included a drip irrigation mainline down the middle and to the sides with a valve that controlled 12 rows, a plastic drip line emitter every 8 feet and a filter and fertilizer injector at the end row.

At that time, when fewer people had the wine knowledge they have today, we thought it practical to provide a description of the types of wines we hoped to produce from these grapes. Since every wine reacts differently to its environment, and seasons and rainfall vary, one can never be 100% certain what the resulting wine will taste like. But we did want to provide a general description, so our future wine audience would know what our goals and expectations were:

Red Wines

Cabernet Sauvignon: Rich and strong, dry (not sweet), quite complex and with a subtle "herbal" quality rather than a fruity one. **It is the basis for France's**

Bordeaux wines, such as the Médocs and St.-Émilions.

Merlot: Although drunk quite often on its own now, at the time we planned to use it for traditional blending with Cabernet Sauvignon, to round out its intense taste and to add a softening and maturing effect. **It is commonly used for blending in the Bordeaux region of France.**

White Wines

Chenin Blanc: Just slightly sweet and fruity, with a simple charm due to its softness and lightness. **This grape is the basis for the Vouvray-style wines of France's Loire Valley.**

Sauvignon Blanc: Also known as Fumé Blanc, it is somewhat dry (not sweet) and has a delicately "smoky" quality and can have a green and herbaceous flavor. **It is the basis for France's white Graves wines.**

Test Block

Our small test block contained Chardonnay Semillon, White Riesling, Colombard, Carnelian, Shiraz, Zinfandel, Grenache, Pinot Noir and U.C. Davis 108. We planned to watch these vines carefully to see which might be good candidates for planting in West Texas vineyards.

(Looking back, I'm quite astonished I did not include full plantings for two of my favorite wines: Pinot Noir and Chardonnay from the Burgundy region of France—Pinot Noir for Bourgogne Rouge and Chardonnay for Bourgogne Blanc.)

Although I don't remember the vine selection discussions precisely, I'm guessing we were looking at producing the wines most popular and salable at the time, and also, we may have been uncertain about having the right soil. The distinctive lime soil in the Burgundy terroir imparts a distinctive flavor.

According to *Wine Folly:* "About 200 million years ago, [Burgundy] was part of a vast, tropical sea … [which created] limestone soils. These soils are the secret behind the zesty minerality that's the hallmark of Burgundy wines. If you venture into the vineyards, you can find chunks of limestone or marl (limestone mixed with clay), that contain fascinating fossilized sea creatures."[4]

Today, however, with advances in wine technology, great Chardonnay is produced worldwide.

When planting, knowing the grapes needed warm sunny days and cool nights during growing season, and seeking protection from frosts and hailstorms that occur frequently in West Texas, we took the following precautions:

- We planted the vineyards with a southeastern exposure to get the needed morning sun without the excessive valley heat.
- We turned the mountain into a protective topographical feature by using it as a shield from the north-born hailstorms.
- By being on the mountain's slope, we attempted to avoid frosts that tend to settle in the valley: This was entirely successful. We also recognized that cultivation on the hillsides limited mechanical harvesters that could not operate on steep terrain. At that time, however, we were not aiming for a volume operation but to prove up the quality potential of Texas wine; some trade-offs seemed inevitable.

I, and the experts who guided me, however, felt the conditions there were very promising. To compare our proposed vineyard location with Napa Valley, California:

- Our mean temperature was the same. Napa had a mean temperature of 60 to 65 degrees Fahrenheit in the growing season. Our mean temperature was the same: an average daily temperature of 75 degrees and 55 degrees at night.
- Napa's soil structure was sandy loam/clay, loan/some gravel. Good water retention and drainage. Enough porosity for deep root

---

4 https://winefolly.com/deep-dive/guide-to-burgundy-wine-with-maps/

penetration. Our soil structure was similar but possibly with better drainage: Silt/loam: 44%, Clay: 23%, Gravel: 33%.

- In Napa, some fumigation was necessary to combat soil diseases. Fortunately, we had virgin soil. Jeff Davis County is one of the very few Texas areas that had not experienced vinifera diseases like root rot—a fungal disease found primarily where cotton has been planted and which can survive many years in the soil and, as roots grow, may start to penetrate that area and then infect the new root; it's present in about 60% of Texas and roughly 90% of the United States. (Later, this area did develop Pierce's disease—a malady caused by a bacterium and spread by leafhoppers that's lethal to grapevines— since no preventive pesticides were administered.)
- We only planted certified heat-treated vines, which destroyed the disease microbes, guarding against inadvertently introducing other areas' soil problems into our own virgin soil.
- The sugar/acid ratio in fruit was good with excellent balance. Our vineyard test plots and first test crushes of grapes indicated our sugar/acid balance was as good as Napa's.

With that relevant data in hand, we were convinced we had a potential winner with our vineyard location. My first goal, however, was to establish that I would actually have a sufficient water source for the cuttings we would plant. All the mountain soil and perfect temperatures in the world won't grow grapes without water. And West Texas is not known for having an abundance of that.

Nevertheless, Blue Mountain's average rainfall was 18 to 19 inches a year, which looked good compared to the 6 to 7 inches in the surrounding areas. But it still was not good enough. That's why we brought in outstanding hydrologist Steve Reed to find underground water for us during our early site evaluation.

And find it he did.

After much exploration, the same degree of nail-biting, breath-holding suspense and possibly as much expense as bringing in an oil gusher, there were soon several operating water wells at our Blue Mountain site. One pumped 60 gallons a minute, from a water zone in the 240- to 280-foot range, making it, at the time, the largest water source in the area. Plenty for the thirstiest of vinifera grapes.

To stretch the water even further, we decided on drip irrigation, a method that was new to West Texas at the time. By now, most people in agribusiness are familiar with this method developed in Israel, which uses only a fraction of the water that conventional irrigation systems require.

There is little loss through evaporation, so it's especially suited to drier areas. The "Key Clip" drip system delivers approximately 1 gallon of water per hour to each vine. A turbulent flow is forced through a small orifice in the emitter. Water is further regulated by 12 different values, each controlling 12 rows of 100 vines.

(For a time, the agriculture experts I dealt with prevailed upon me to become somewhat of a drip irrigation evangelist, flying me in to different Rotary Club, Chamber of Commerce and other meetings to give slide presentations on the benefits of drip irrigation, which eventually would become more prevalent in West Texas.)

Ultimately, we built a steel-frame farm building with an office, which eventually would have a tiny lab and several insulated stainless-steel tanks for experimental wine testing and production.

A Milestone Opening Ceremony

In April 1977, Glasscock Vineyards held an opening ceremony with about 250 state officials, wine enthusiasts, Texas wine activists, university professors working on vineyard wine experimentation and local, as well as other Texas, ranchers. I had small planes ferrying in family members and others came by train to Alpine, about 24 miles away, where we dispatched a driver to pick them up and bring them to Fort Davis and Blue Mountain. I maintained a small, two-bedroom apartment in Fort Davis, where I held meetings and could accommodate a few guests. Beyond that, there was historic Hotel Limpia with 30 rooms and state park–operated Indian Lodge with 39 rooms. Most guests had to spread out to the nearby towns of Alpine and Marfa if they chose to stay overnight.

Members of the El Paso symphony came in to play on the hillside for the opening ceremony, a quite festive event, as it was the realization of a long-held dream, not just for me, but for many who wished to see life and promise brought back into the area of natural grandeur and rich history. At sunset, beautiful tones of gold and soft purple lighting illuminated the mountainside to create a memorable and historic moment. It was a milestone event for the fledging Texas wine industry. It demonstrated we could not only create a premium vineyard, we could attract key players and influencers and create a buzz—something that would serve us well in the days and months ahead.

We believed that we were acting not just on behalf of ourselves and other wine enthusiasts, but by introducing a high-profit crop like vinifera grapes to West Texas, we ultimately would enable more people to remain on the land their families had farmed for generations. An agribusinessman or -woman with a passion for excellence and a bit of an adventurous spirit would not be forced to migrate to the cities in order to seek a job and survive financially. In short, we thought our research and planting would be good for everyone.

Acknowledgement by Texas A & M: Another Napa

Later, Ron Perry, a horticulturist with Texas A & M University and one of the two authors of the Texas A & M study, which had first identified all of Texas as a Region V, later revised the study to indicate a variety of different Texas wine regions.

After the planting of our vineyard, Ron wrote to me: "I concede you have established what appears to be another Napa Valley. I also applaud your meticulous methods in accomplishing this task."

Kudos to Ron Perry for his gracious concession, for the revision of the wine grape feasibility study and for his continued work and research into developing fine wines in Texas, a valuable contribution.

Pilgrims and Wine Gurus Come to Inspect

The establishment of a new premium wine grape–growing region, with many of the climate and even some of the soil characteristics of Napa and parts of France, created quite a buzz in the world of wine lovers. In fact, many of the curious came from faraway places just to see and experience what we had achieved.

One day, when I had just arrived at my vineyard and was walking through to inspect the vines, I saw movement behind a plant. I reached forward and held it aside and there were two Japanese tourists, cameras dangling from their necks, who had journeyed to see for themselves this new premium vineyard and wine region. No doubt, the Texas location and tales of Western lore had factored into their decision to make this visit. Of course, I overcame my surprise and welcomed them, although there definitely was a language barrier.

A really memorable moment came when Peter Sichel, owner of Blue Nun winery, once producing the best-selling wine in the world, decided to visit and inspect my vineyard and the West Texas, Davis Mountains and High Plains area of Texas. Like big ranchers, always searching for cheaper land to raise cattle, exploring Australia and other countries, I know Peter traveled continuously, in Europe, Canada, the Far East, Australia and New Zealand. This was partly to judge wine competitions, be an ambassador for his brand, Blue Nun, and taste last year's crop from the various wine-growing regions. And I suspect part of it, at least, was looking for cheaper land to grow grapes and also different countries to source wine to hedge against possible shortages.

Peter was sophisticated, tall and debonair, much like David Niven, a movie star of an earlier era, or perhaps Pierce Brosnan of today or when Brosnan portrayed James Bond's 007. He was, without a doubt, the most famous person in the wine business of that era. His photo appeared in magazines and wine calendars, and he judged many U.S. and international wine competitions, including the International Wine and Spirit Competition in London.

I had met Peter in Mainz, Germany, at Blue Nun, his family's wine business, established in 1857, when I went with other winemakers to the Wine Festival in

Vevey, Switzerland. When he contacted me and told me he planned a Texas visit, I was very excited to learn we would have one of the top wine producers and wine celebrities in the world inspecting our vineyards, climate conditions and resulting grape quality in Texas.

And what I learned from Peter was not just about wine. When I went to meet Peter at his plane from New York City arriving at the San Antonio airport, I got a crash course in one of the reasons he was such a big celebrity. As we walked down the long corridor from his gate, Peter launched into a story I would always remember and which I came to understand as one crucial factor in becoming successful.

"Last night was so hectic" he began, just after getting off his plane and greeting me. "My children were afraid I would have a heart attack. I arrived at a large meeting place in New York City and, to my surprise, they were holding a major event to honor me for my many contributions to organizations in that city."

Peter was giving me his elevator pitch. One has to understand, at that time, he was the most famous person in the world of wine. His photo was everywhere. And he was coming to San Antonio, to meet with me and learn more about Texas wine. I had already met him at his family business. So, clearly, I knew who he was. But Peter felt it necessary anyway to give me his elevator speech, clearly setting out his stellar credentials.

It was a good lesson for me. Women, at least up to that time, were raised to be modest, demure, more often seen than heard in the company of men. Women, even Nobel Prize or Pulitzer Prize winners, tended to be modest, never mentioning their accomplishments, possibly secretly relying on the fact that you might be aware of them, which most never were. Men, on the other hand, were steeped in the knowledge they had to "toot their own horn." They did it about their golf games and drinking prowess and, more boldly and ardently, about their careers. They knew they had to establish their credentials, swiftly and decisively, hopefully to dominate the conversation and achieve their goal. What is the goal of a meeting, some books of the time asked? "To win it" was the correct answer.

Years later, when I developed the website AdvancingWomen.com (which I will be discussing later), with the goal of leveling the playing field for women and helping mentor them in their careers, I would remember Peter's elevator pitch.

"Modesty does not create opportunity" was an empirical fact, confirmed by the 2000 The Winds of Change Foundation collaborative study with the Center for Research on Women at Wellesley examining the experiences of well-recognized women leaders.

In those early days of the Net, I mentored career women in many areas, including what email was and how to use it. But one of the most crucial attributes to develop was found in Peter Sichel's lesson. Put modesty aside and always give your elevator pitch.

I explained it didn't matter how you segued into it or how far afield from the subject at hand; the flimsiest of segues could get you to it.

For example: "I don't believe I've ever been so hot since the air-conditioner went out when they were giving me that big award at …"

Mission accomplished. You had credentials. You were someone to be reckoned with. Remember it and deal with it.

With the visits of Peter Sichel and other wine figures to Texas, and with the California wine industry graciously cheering us on, Texas vineyards and wineries definitely were on the map.

Now, we had to develop an infrastructure to support our nascent wine industry.

Communications Team - Educating Stakeholders

At that point, we had a number of small vineyards and many test vineyards throughout the state. But what we did not have was an infrastructure to support the wine industry. More particularly, we did not have laws that would enable a wine industry to be born, thrive and be profitable.

Once again, Texas was fortunate in that we had Leon Adams, wine production advocate and the author of *The Wines of America*, who had studied wines, wineries and wine laws in every state, and who could point us to the goalposts in enabling the creation of this new industry.

Thanks to Leon's support and advice, we knew we were going to have to change Texas legislation, which no one had been able to change in a hundred years. This was going to be a heavy lift. And we could not do it alone without widespread support.

And how were we going to get widespread support on a topic about which most of the public knew very little? Not much was known, even in agribusiness.

Supporters who were, at least, somewhat familiar with the basic concepts of the wine business and its potential benefits would be a critical component in passage of any bill addressing these issues.

We decided our first challenge would be to educate the public and a wide range of various stakeholders about the benefits to each of them of establishing a wine industry in Texas.

With that imperative in mind, we turned to experts in communication for help. The first place we sought help was the Ed Yardang group, headed by Lionel Sosa, who was fast becoming a legend with his uncanny insight and ability to communicate complex ideas to ordinary folks in an appealing and graphically striking and inspiring way. Also contributing to top level management, creativity and inspiration were partners Beverly (Bev) Coiner and Warren Stewart. This group really set the pace for stylish and impactful communication in South Texas for both local and national accounts at that time. I was very gratified that the entire team immediately understood, and adopted for their own, our vision of Texas' potential to produce fine wines.

Their vision was to define Texas stakeholders and communicate that vision in a way that explained the potential benefits of this new industry and get others on board who could become a voice to influence their legislators.

Again, thanks to Leon Adams, we understood our task was to reach out to ordinary citizens, farmers, ranchers, students and universities and clearly display to them that a wine industry in Texas would benefit all of us. We wanted to define ourselves and not let anyone else define us as a move geared toward "wine snobs" or those who lived off their trust accounts and sipped expensive wines at ritzy restaurants or country clubs. This had to be a farm winery and grassroots movement that, like a rising tide, would "lift all boats."

And, because it was true, it was an easy argument to make, although it took a lot of work to produce it and get it out to all our constituencies, month after month, through both research and speaking visits throughout the state, but particularly in West Texas; through monthly newsletters updating stakeholders on progress in the Texas wine scene; and through the media, that, at that moment, had a great thirst for this newest development on the Texas scene.

First, we wanted to tie the production of fine wine to the care and husbandry of land, specifically Texas land.

When we started a conversation with our stakeholders, it was important to introduce me, the messenger, our earth-friendly philosophy and the economic potential it presented for all of our state. Part of this education also served to "anoint the messenger." "I'm on your side. This is not about anyone getting a bigger slice of the pie; this is about creating a bigger pie."

The economics were undeniable.

At that time, in the mid-seventies:

- California wine shipments had doubled in the past 10 years.
- The acreage of wine grapes had more than doubled.
- California had shipped 288.6 million gallons of wine to all markets in the previous year The estimated wholesale value of that wine was $1 billion, the retail value an estimated 1.8 billion.
- Of all this California wine, Texas consumed 13 million gallons at an average price of $3.25 a bottle. That's $40 million dollars, or a portion thereof, we could have kept in our own state if we could supply our own wine.

Another financial impact was that the creation of a vineyard, at that time, could transform $300-an-acre land into $8,000-an-acre land or above. That would create a significant impact for the state, not to mention the development of support industries and jobs.

What was not to like?

Then, there was our earth-friendly philosophy.

For four generations, the Glasscock family had been closely tied to the soil, through cattle, ranching and minerals. I understood that, when nature is treated respectfully, animal life, plant life and my family and business thrived.

My communications team and I wanted people to know I was not just a messenger but an advocate. I set out to form an agribusiness that was based on a balanced ecosystem, bound in a cycle of health and reproduction. An ordered diversity was the key in the first conceptualization and resultant system of management of our vineyards.

- Native trees in the Blue Mountain area would be maintained for shade and windbreaks, and for the shelter they give to wildlife. When necessary, they would also be used for food, lumber, fence posts and firewood.

- No inhumane treatment of wildlife would be allowed.
- Cover crops such as clover would be used to return nitrogen to the soil. (Nitrogen is a major nutrient of grapes.)
- Proper tillage, rotation and return of organic wastes such as stems and seeds from crushed grapes would reduce the need for fertilizer from outside sources.
- Drip irrigation would be installed to utilize and conserve precious water, in the hope this water conservation practice would spread and allow the planting of more vines and crops.
- All roads would follow the contour of the land in order to reduce erosion. Tanks and buildings would be designed to blend in, not detract from, the sweep and majesty of the West Texas landscape.
- There would be a continuous and ongoing evaluation of solar and wind to meet future energy needs.
- When possible, area skills in crafts such as wood carving would be supported and used.

The end result of these practices would be to define ourselves, and our wine and grape industry, as an integral part of the land. Instead of an obsession with production and expansion, we would try to temper such needs with a more complex awareness of the needs of the future.

Those needs entailed ecological, nutritional, technological appropriateness, social stability skills, quality, thrift, diversity and decentralization.

We believed that our pioneering work in proving the viability of West Texas vineyards ultimately would allow more family members to stay on and make a living from their generationally passed-down family farms and ranches.

At that time, Texas media displayed a great interest in following vineyard and wine developments in Texas. In fact, some media from other areas, particularly California, seemed intrigued or, at least, paid attention as well. We were written up in *Wine Spectator* and *The Wine Investor* and by various wine writers, as well as financial writers in California as well as Texas.

We saw it as a critical part of our job to tell a compelling story so there would be a large, grassroots audience that would support the creation of a wine industry in Texas. We also knew we were going to have to make some major changes in our state's laws and infrastructure if we wanted to be successful and that we would need popular support to do it. *Skies of Tejas Airlines* magazine, in their October 1979 cover article, "Glasscock Wine Country," referred to our continuing communications with different stakeholders:

> "Gretchen was in the unique position of speaking two vastly different English languages—scientific jargon and West Texas slang.

> "Gretchen Glasscock stands squarely between the professors and the ranchers, often as an interpreter. How many women can dismount a horse after managing a 20,000-cattle ranch in South Texas all day and whip out a degree from Columbia University?"

(Although much appreciated, this description overstates my equestrian skills and probably is a product of its diplomatic author being on the side of a wine industry in Texas; nonetheless, I'll gratefully take it.)

Who Will Educate the Bankers?

I do think the author got it right, however, that I (supported by my communications team) had assumed the role of an interpreter between different audiences. One of the groups we saw as stakeholders were Texas bankers and financial organizations who, at that time, had no clue how to loan to vineyards because they were unfamiliar with all the financials and complexities: costs, risks, potential profits. This is actually not at all unusual for banks. For many years it had been exactly the same in the oil and gas industry, where, if you wanted a loan on an oil and gas property, you had to go to Dallas to get it. Local banks were fine if you wanted a loan on a car or a boat, particularly if you were in the military. If you wanted a loan against raw land and there was enough of it, you could get a loan on it. It doesn't take a rocket scientist or a great deal of expertise to loan on land. But just as local banks weren't interested in oil and gas properties in a previous time, neither were they interested in wine finance nor very interested in learning about it.

That same *Skies of Tejas Airlines* magazine article quoted me as saying:

> "Many people think that bankers are afraid of losing money, but my experience has been they are more frightened of being laughed at. All the banking guys have lost money on corporations and that's OK, but nobody wants to be the first one to lose money on grapes."

But, just as, eventually, some banks became experts in the oil and gas business, eventually some would go on to become experts in the vineyard and wine business and then, hopefully, it would become a point of pride to have the knowledge to be able to loan money on it. French, Belgian and European banks have learned to lend money on wine and U.S. banks, always conservative and cautious, like most banks, began the learning curve. In California, Bank of America made its "first [wine] inventory loan ... to Stag's Leap Wine Cellars in 1974, permitting them to hold and age the Cabernets that would beat Château Mouton Rothschild in the 1976 Bicentennial blind tasting in Paris that skyrocketed Napa's wines to world rank."[5] Even then, as one of the bank officers noted: "They were placing the same collateral value on a ten dollar bottle of wine as a two dollar bottle of wine. You'd only get one dollar instead of five, to work with, even after the Paris triumph. And the winery business is very much a financing business. Someone had to supply capital for extended periods."[6]

This unfortunate financing disparity existed in California, which was decades ahead of Texas in the wine business. One easily can imagine the state of wine banking in Texas at the time. Nonexistent.

In the meantime, it was a pretty hardscrabble existence trying to finance a vineyard. Businessmen, naturally, were interested in making money, and wine making in Texas wasn't proven. Even venture capitalists, in the business of placing money bets on unproven businesses, were not interested in such a long game: three to five years from the planting of a vine until a usable crop; four years for a red wine to develop and be ready. A person or an investor must be willing to invest a decade or more to enjoy the multiple fruits of his or her labor. Banks weren't going for it. One had to find one's own financing with one's own money or holdings. And some might say, "That's fair. After all it's your gamble." True, but difficult. One had to

---

5 Moira Johnson, *The Tumultuous History of the Bank of America* (Beard Books, Frederick, Maryland, 2000).

6 Moira Johnson, *The Tumultuous History of the Bank of America* (Beard Books, Frederick, Maryland, 2000).

borrow or liquidate a portion of one's assets to keep going. And always, one had to weigh the size of the gamble with its effect on one's family and other business, the one that actually did make money and support that family. Each new investment had to be weighed carefully and in context. One had to dig deep to keep going.

Wine Ambassadors - Texas Wine Becomes Part of the Conversation

And one had to keep moving toward one's goals. Like some of the other Texas wine activists, I explored other wine regions looking for answers that could help us in Texas. And this learning venture was a two-way street. Just as Texas wine activists learned about other wine regions, some of us, certainly Dr. Bobby Smith of La Buena Vida Vineyards and I, and possibly others, were emissaries, spreading the word about the possibilities of the fledgling Texas wine industry to these established wine regions. I visited many of California wineries, from the largest to the boutique wineries in Napa and Sonoma and then the new Callaway Vineyard & Winery in Temecula, California, which entrepreneur Ely Callaway had researched and planted. His groundbreaking work went a long way toward establishing Southern California's South Coast, with its cooling Pacific Ocean air providing a microclimate conducive to growing fine wine grapes. Although Callaway was, at the time, the newest winery on the scene, California vintners remembered well their challenging journey of establishing themselves as a viable premium wine region and seemed empathetic with the journey Texas was about to begin. Ely Callaway, in particular, seemed very happy to meet us and wish us well on our quest. During our visit in 1976, he insisted that I put on a Callaway T-shirt he had just gifted me with, which I did, with pleasure.

I also accompanied some members of the pioneering Wente family of California and other California vintners to Europe and its very mature wine industry with the ultimate goal of attending the Wine Festival in Vevey, Switzerland, a once-in-a-generation event, held only every 20 years. According to the festival website: "Recognized by UNESCO on its list of intangible cultural heritage, the Fête des Vignerons brings generations together, connecting people from the villages, the countryside and the vineyards, locals and foreigners, and offers each one the opportunity to go beyond himself, to transcend and collectively participate in a show unique in the world."[7]

On the way to Vevey, we toured other wine areas and met with or were fêted by other vintners and suppliers, including Peter Sichel of Blue Nun, then, as mentioned, owner of the best-selling international wine in the world. We were treated like royalty by the GEA Westfalia Separator company in beautiful Westphalia, Germany, originally formed in 1893 and a worldwide leader in the production of centrifuges, which are used to clarify and spin out impurities in a vast range of products including in the production of wine. I was told the company treated us with such exquisite care and hospitality because the multibillion-dollar wine company Gallo spends so much money there. We were thought of not just as tiny or aspiring, or even established vintners, but as ambassadors from the larger U.S. wine industry. Thanks, I presume, to Gallo, our trip included a meeting with Westfalia Separator's president, in his huge and ornate office, a lively party with local music and dancing at an authentically picturesque Westphalian home. Each of us was escorted full-time by a local president based in one of the many countries in which they did business. I think my escort headed up centrifuge sales in Japan. I was somewhat nonplussed when I needed a quick haircut and he dutifully insisted on accompanying me to the salon where he stood by, very gregarious and making light conversation in several languages while a young woman clipped my hair.

When we arrived in Vevey, Switzerland, we also were fêted by Nestlé, the multinational food and beverage processing company, the largest food company in the world. Nestlé has over 2,000 brands, including a plethora of products like chocolate, baby food, coffee, ice cream, pet food and water. Not surprisingly, it wanted to enter the wine business and did so by acquiring the Beringer brand, its wineries and vineyards in 1971. This was quite a coup, considering that Beringer also owned the brand names of Meridian, Napa Ridge, Chateau Souverain, Chateau St. Jean and Stags' Leap. The latter two, in particular, would score global success and recognition in the Judgement of Paris in 1976.

With these high-profile hosts and industry titans paying tribute to the upstart wine business in the United States, and principally in California, there was generally a blurb in local newspapers all along our trip from England, throughout Germany,

---

7 Fête des Vignerons 2019, www.fetedesvignerons.ch/en

saying something like: "California vintners and Texas vintner arrive in Europe, to taste our wines and visit some of our renowned wine support services." By the time we arrived in Vevey, Switzerland, the local paper announced: "Texas vintner arrives accompanied by California vintners." It seems, at that time in Europe, all things Texas were much in vogue. And sure enough, when the grand parade at the Vevey Festival took place, one of the lead characters marching in the parade was a giant Texas cowboy, wearing boots and a Stetson and sporting a pistol. We had, symbolically, entered into wine history. Now, Texas wine was part of the story.

We had always believed Texas was fully capable of developing a wine industry that, eventually, could compete with the finest wines from California and France. We still had to prove ourselves as winegrowers and serious premium wine makers, but now we had captured the attention and interest of the finest, most honored, recognized and tradition-bound wine makers in the world. They were, at the very least, curious. What could these Texans, with their outsized Stetsons, boots and wine ambitions, produce if they set their minds to it?

Our representation, and the Vevey celebration's spoofing, friendly acceptance of us at that global, prestigious and once-in-a-generation event, provided us with a much higher profile and wind at our back for the battles to come.

Now, as we continued to report in our newsletter, "Gretchen's Grapevine," events like our attendance at the Vevey, Switzerland, wine festival, some European vintners, many of our California colleagues and allies and, eventually, many of our Texas stakeholders began to look forward eagerly and with anticipation to our communications and our progress. We hoped many of them later would lend us their support. And they did, when the fledgling wine industry faced its biggest challenge.

CHAPTER FIVE

Epic Battle – Historic Victory

Going Up Against A Global Empire
with Unsavory Roots

As the Texas Legislature convened in 1979 and we Texas wine activists began to form our agenda, the deep expertise and active participation of Leon Adams, author of *The Wines of America*, was invaluable.

Instead of attempting to research all the laws that would either hinder or allow a wine industry to flourish, I once again turned to Leon. He told me that, based on his knowledge of wine growing and sales in every state, the following was necessary, and he also set that out in his book:

> "Whether a small wine grower profit[s] or lose[s] depends on many factors, including their talent, industrious habits, business sense, and particularly on whether the law of the state where the small winery is situated favors farm wineries with a reasonable license fee. ... The law must permit the winegrower to offer complimentary tasting, to sell his product at both retail and wholesale, and to stay open on Sunday because that is the day most people like to go on wine tours."[8]

Typically small wineries were selling 10% of their wine at the winery but making 30% of their profit there. In order to succeed, as Leon pointed out, having gotten

---

8 Adams, *The Wines of America*, 2nd Edition, 543.

the advice from wine pioneer Herman Wente, the winemaker must be able to sell his wines at retail: "Thereby he makes not only the profits (if any) of the grape grower and of the wine producer, but the profits of the wholesaler and of the retailer in addition."[9]

One could see how this system would not be favored by wholesalers and retailers. Although, as the wine industry grew, wine sold from the winery would only be a tiny fraction of that available to be sold through giant liquor chains. One could argue that selling from a winery, creating a tourist destination, would raise the profile of the winery, increase awareness of its brand and, ultimately, its sale price from a traditional retail store.

But the fact was the liquor lobby paid good money to its lobbyists to be staunch enemies of any new wine legislation and to block it with a vengeance. And they were good at what they did—or what they blocked—as no one had been able to pass new wine legislation in Texas in a century.

The battle was soon to be joined.

Experts warned me that this was going to be an uphill fight, with well-financed and powerful opposition and little chance of actually succeeding.

I needed to educate myself and take a clear-eyed look at what I was about to be up against. Now, looking back on that fight, I think I was so determined and so filled with adrenaline that I didn't fully realize the scope of the forces lining up against me. At least my actions didn't reflect it.

Instead, I declared I was going "to take the bull by the horns" and get the legislation passed. There was no way over, around or under it. If we wanted a successful wine industry, we had to enact legislation that empowered it, instead of being crippled by laws designed and largely passed by the liquor lobby, meant to severely limit, contain and weaken a native wine industry.

By now, due to a long and successful campaign of communicating the relevant facts and the many benefits to farmers, ranchers, consumers and taxpayers, we had the widespread grassroots support we had sought in order to pass legislation that would empower a financially viable wine industry in Texas.

The same, unfortunately, could not be said of the liquor industry or the liquor lobby. Bear in mind, we are not talking about a local skirmish or a petty dustup between opposing interests. We are talking about a global liquor empire that was awash in money, power, muscle and legislative experience in how to rout any

---

9 Adams, *The Wines of America*, 2nd Edition, 543.

would-be start-ups that might challenge their dominance of the alcoholic beverage markets and how they worked.

Today, the alcoholic beverage industry has taken on a certain sheen and aura of style and sophistication with the upscaling of American drinking habits with brands like Chivas Regal and Crown Royal. But that is not the whole story. The liquor industry in America had some unsavory roots in bootlegging during Prohibition, practiced by people like Edgar Bronfman and Joe Kennedy and their respective clans, who later bought or gave their way into respectability.

And the liquor industry didn't hesitate to try to intimidate anyone whose interests did not align with their own.

According to Frank Parlato, an investigative journalist whose work has been published in major publications all over the world, including *The New York Times*, CNN, Fox News, *Rolling Stone*, and *People* magazine, "Sam [Bronfman] and his brothers cut distribution deals with Arnold Rothstein, Meyer Lansky, Charles 'Lucky' Luciano, and Arthur 'Dutch Schultz' Flegenheimer. … Al Capone ran Bronfman booze from Saskatchewan to Minneapolis then to Chicago using cars, trucks and the Soo line. Benjamin 'Bugs' Siegel and Lansky protected Bronfman liquor shipments across the border against hijackers. … Lansky and 'Bugs' Siegel … formed … a regulatory commission to police 'free enterprise' advocates who might try to buck the syndicate and interfere with booze sales."[10]

Well, that was bracing to know.

By the 1970s Seagram was the world's largest and most successful liquor distribution system on Earth, with its powerful tentacles everywhere

Nicholas Faith, author of *The Rise and Fall of the House of Seagram*, describes how, when he told friends he'd been commissioned to write about the Bronfmans, "Friends muttered 'cement galoshes' and one banker suggested that they'd take out a contract on [me]."[11]

That kind of reputation of the liquor industry's colorful past certainly got one's attention. Author Nicholas Faith concluded, or, at the very least, hoped those extreme measures were from a previous era. However, in his view, a "continuing atmosphere of threat and mystery" still pervaded the industry."[12] I went with the theory that, with the legality and increased respectability of the liquor industry and

---

10 https://frankreport.com/2018/01/17/the-true-history-and-sinister-origin-of-bronfman-family-wealth/

11 https://www.spearswms.com/the-bronfmans-the-rise-and-fall-of-the-house-of-seagram/

12 Faith, Nicholas. *The Bronfmans (*St. Martin's Publishing Group. Kindle Edition), p. 1.

the rising profile of some of its brightest luminaries, its tactics had changed. In the new era, persuasion was not as brutal and intimidation was more subtle. However, the strategy was still the same: Kill new legislation and block change.

One of the liquor lobby tactics I was told about, but can't confirm, was that a liquor store or chain would be warned that if they sold a certain brand of wine, they would not be delivered Chivas Regal or other Scotch or premium alcohol at Christmas time, their biggest and most profitable sales season. In other words, hit them in the pocketbooks.

Armed with this knowledge about the liquor industry, and the Texas liquor lobby in particular, I set about seeing how I could overcome this challenge and succeed in getting my legislation passed.

Choosing the Legislative Team –
Our Band of Warriors

The first step was to hire Pike Powers, legislative counsel from the firm of Fulbright & Jaworski in Austin. Later Powers was named 2017 Texan of the Year by the Texas Legislative Conference. Pike was known for putting Austin on the tech map. According to a 2016 article in the New Braunfels *Herald-Zeitung:* "He was instrumental in attracting MCC, 3M, Sematech and Applied Materials, as well as AMD and Samsung expansions and other manufacturing and research operations to Austin,"[13] thrusting the state capital into the epicenter of the sizzling hot tech economy, right behind Silicon Valley. Less known is his critical role in creating, shaping and shepherding through the historic Farm Winery Act.

Pike connected me and helped form a legislative team to sponsor my bill and push it forward. The team included Representative John Wilson, named by *Texas Monthly* in 1977 as one of the "Best" legislators, who was on the House Committee on Liquor Regulation; Jim Nowlin, a previous member of the Liquor Regulation

---

13 http://herald-zeitung.com/community_alert/article_c715d470-bb58-11e6-84b3-7f56986354f4.html

Committee, who went on to become a judge of the U.S. District Court, Western District of Texas; and Senator John Traeger, an Air Force Vet, also serving in the Texas National Guard.

As we began to work the halls of the Texas Legislature, I also found a colleague and a supportive professional friend in my own Bexar County Rep, Frank Tejeda. Frank was warm and personable and a true warrior, a Marine Corps vet who had been awarded a Purple Heart, among other honors.

Luckily for me, in the legislature's 66th Regular Session (R.S.) in 1979, Tejeda was Vice Chair of the Liquor Regulation Committee, the committee that would first hear my bill and decide on whether to send it out from committee for a vote—in other words, the committee that initially had sole control over the life or death of my bill. Tejeda's position on that committee meant I had several allies on the inside updating me on either progress or roadblocks put in the way of my bill so I had advance warning and could try to counter any specific negative tactics before they took permanent hold and halted the bill in its tracks.

Crucially, looking back on this time, what I had was a team of fierce warriors determined to succeed and undeterred by the firepower and odds stacked against us.

Strategic Elements of Our Farm Winery Bill

Our first task was to write the bill itself and incorporate the 27 necessary changes in alcoholic beverages laws to align it with the tenets Leon Adams has presented that would enable a successful wine industry in Texas. One specific: We took into account the needs of those vintners, like Dr. Bobby Smith, always very supportive, whose vineyards were located in dry counties, including provisions that would allow them to produce and bottle wine but only distribute them outside the dry county. This position allowed us to achieve the desired result, at the same time sidestepping the precarious strategy of attempting anything that would impinge on keeping dry counties dry, which could have brought on overwhelming opposition instead of over-whelming support. Pike Powers and his team put this and all the other sought-after changes in the law through a computer and produced a bill that would accomplish them all, maintaining the delicate wet/dry county dichotomy.

Creation of the Texas Grape Growers Association

Next, Pike advised me that, instead of this being seen as a major push for and by one individual, Gretchen Glasscock, we would fare a lot better if we could cite the support of a group. I knew from Leon Adams that the closer we could align ourselves with the agricultural industry, the greater our chances of success. I set about calling the Texas wine activists I had met, including Dr. Bobby Smith, Ed Auler and Doc McPherson, and explained where we were in this process, the game plan and the general strategy of the naming and specifics of the Texas Farm Winery Bill. And that was how the "Texas Grape Growers" organization was born. From that moment on, at every point in the process of our bill, the "Texas Grape Growers," which was basically just a handful of us grape growers, with no formal charter, agenda or organization, put out a congratulatory statement, praising our goals, cheering us on to success.

In the June 1979 issue of Southwest Airlines' inflight magazine, a sidebar entitled "Close Call for a Wine Bill" covered my address to the legislature, outlining the specifics of the Farm Winery Bill and the practical rationale behind each provision:

> "Basically, the bill eliminates class designations for winery permits, enabling wineries to buy grapes from outside sources and allowing them to sell directly to the consumer.

> "In her address before the legislature, Glasscock pointed out that the laws prohibited a winery from purchasing grapes or juice from another grower.

> "'If you have a vineyard, you must have a winery,' she said. 'Even 120 acres might require a small winery which could cost $1 million to construct. So one must either bring in grapes or juice from elsewhere or ask an investor

to let his $1 million investment sit idle for a good part of 8 years.'

"She also said that laws cannot limit purchase of grapes to "Texas" grapes, because there simply aren't enough. 'It's also necessary, on occasion, to purchase grapes because of crop failure, drought or, if the grapes in a given year do not have the correct sugar-acid ratio.' Glasscock added, a small winery must be permitted to sell to consumers from its own premises. She explained, 'In Napa, 10% of the wine produced is sold from the winery door, but it earns 30% of their profits.'"

Since, at that point, we had broad popular support, and in order not to wake a sleeping tiger, we had designed the bill so it did not challenge the wet/dry precincts, a hot button issue in Texas. Now, we had clearly staked out our position. We targeted constituencies and stakeholders throughout the state, from agribusiness people to universities, to community leaders and chambers of commerce, to wine lovers. We also targeted legislators who had expressed support for a change that would add revenue, tourism and enhanced lifestyle to the state and, in many cases, to the district each represented. The single group that opposed this change, silent up to this point, was the liquor lobby.

The Battle Was Now Joined

I knew it would be tough and very consequential. I guess my Columbia University literary education had an enduring effect on me at critical times because I couldn't help recalling the St. Crispin's Day Speech of Shakespeare's *Henry V,* in which the king urges his men on to battle, despite the scars they, no doubt, would receive and because of the honor they would earn in battle that day. He rouses his men to a glorious future for those who, even in aging, would lay bare their arms and show their scars, proudly, for they would always be remembered as warriors and heroes who rose to the challenge and bravely fought a ferocious battle.

With those words in mind, I would remember my team of warriors who were about to go up against the very powerful liquor lobby. In particular, they were and I was about to confront "Butch" Sparks, tough, battle-hardened, longtime liquor lobbyist. According to a *Texas Weekly* article, Butch, a lawyer, was "employed as the Executive Director of the Licensed Beverage Distributors for more than 33 years, lobbying in Texas and Washington, D.C. He was also a member of the Board of Directors of the Austin Club"[14]—providing him with prominent local contacts, connections and influencers.

Butch was highly paid, well organized and deadly efficient. Like all lobbyists, he was a constant presence in the legislature and part of the process, intimately involved with the care and feeding of legislators who had control of his area of interest, the liquor industry. At that moment, he had only one job and that was to kill the Farm Winery Bill. He was a formidable opponent.

Confrontation and Victory

Butch's first move was to get my bill sent to the House Committee on Liquor Regulation, popularly dubbed the "graveyard committee" because that is where alcohol-related bills were sent to die. At least, that was the liquor lobby's standard operating procedure.

From that moment forward, my life became a perpetual race to drive an hour and 15 minutes from San Antonio, my home, to the legislature in Austin, to attend whatever impromptu and strategically timed session their chairman, Bill Coody, threw at me.

I am not one to hurl stones at the dearly departed, particularly if it's only because their interests did not align with mine. But Bill Coody was, it turns out, an adversary who, for whatever reason—there were many, I can guess—was determined not to let my bill out of his committee. Bill Coody is quoted as quipping, "No man's life,

---

14 https://texasweekly.texastribune.org/texas-weekly/vol-25/no-37/people/

liberty or property were safe when the Texas Legislature was in session."[15]

I guess I could take that as fair warning. So I embarked on my sprint to keep up with the committee by arriving at all of their hearings, many scheduled at 2:00 a.m.

And whenever I arrived at the Capitol, there always was either Butch Sparks or two of his henchmen lying in wait for my arrival, then following me wherever I went.

For a woman, alone, at 2:00 a.m., going up an elevator in the Capitol with two men who never greeted or acknowledged me except with a fishy sideways glance every now and then, could be a disconcerting experience. It was especially disconcerting, if one happened to recall the somewhat unsavory history of the origins of the liquor business and all the muscle they used in those days to enforce their dominance in the alcohol distribution system. What exactly did these guys have in mind, following me around the Capitol day after day, or night after night?

Fortunately, however I might have felt, or whatever I might have suspected, outwardly I had somewhat the opposite reaction.

One night in the elevator, I broke the silence with these two guys:

"Look," I said. "I don't know what you two guys have in mind or what it is you are trying to accomplish, but whatever it is, you might as well just get on with it, because I definitely am not going to stop trying to get my bill passed."

They just stared silently and glumly at me.

Judging from the events that transpired later, I think the message was received. I wasn't quitting.

"This is starting to look endless," I thought as this legislative session inched toward its closing days, "and they could just run out the clock." I decided to "confront the tiger in his lair."

I waited in a Capitol hallway for an opportunity to appear in Bill Coody's office and ask him myself when he was planning to let my Farm Winery Bill come out.

Chairman Coody, like all the other legislators, was, I'm sure, beloved by his wife, family and friends and probably many colleagues. However, with me, he chose to adopt a stern, grumpy and thoroughly unpleasant attitude that I took was meant to convey that he had more important things to do than waste his time talking with a woman about some stupid bill that was slated to die anyway. He may have thought that would be sufficient for me just to give up, either in disgust or hopelessness or because it was deliberately insulting and rude, and who wants to put up with that?

There was little, if any, conversation coming from him, not even bland pleas-

15 https://obituaries.weatherforddemocrat.com/obituary/w-g-coody-729354222

antries or, on the other end of the spectrum, convenient lies promising an outcome he had no intention of delivering.

I got it.

"Look," I said, "you can either deal with me, or the next face you see will be from *Sixty Minutes.*" And I walked out.

Much later that evening, when Frank Tejeda passed me in the hallway, he smiled broadly and said: "Hey, your bill is coming out tomorrow morning."

I almost fainted. Well, not really. I was surprised for a moment, but then I realized, having a graveyard committee that can literally kill and bury bills is a very valuable political asset for the liquor lobby. Better to let one bill through than risk your entire killing system. Besides, there still might be ways to stop it or water it down beyond recognition. It was not a victory, at that point, for the liquor lobby, but they hadn't yet lost the whole game either.

At this point, now that the bill had emerged from committee, most of the shepherding of the bill was passed on to my legislative warriors who were ready for battle and did a superb job.

However, not surprisingly, now that the bill was out of committee, and having a somewhat realistic chance of passing, or at least being voted on, the liquor lobby struck the first blow. Doing their bidding, Dallas Senator Oscar Mauzy "tagged" the bill, tantamount to killing it. A tag prohibits the bill from being heard for at least 48 hours unless the tag is removed by the initiator. (My warrior) Representative Wilson countered by knocking eight of Mauzy's bills off the House calendar. That got Mauzy's attention. Finally, it appeared Mauzy concluded that sacrificing eight bills for one, particularly one that no one else objected to, was not going to be a winning strategy, so he removed his tag. House Bill 2229 was set to move straight into the State Affairs Committee.

At this time, I was sitting in my office in San Antonio, on Broadway, next to the phone. It seemed everything was moving along on track and my legislative team, with quick, bold, aggressive action, was getting the bill through.

Then, my phone rang.

"Hello." It was Billy Clayton, Speaker of the Texas House. I had met him previously in West Texas, where we had some conversations about water resources.

"Gretchen," he said, "a fist fight has broken out in the House. Can you please come in and negotiate this legislation?"

"Yes," I said. "But what happened?

"Dallas Senator O. H. Harris tagged your bill and Representative John Wilson went over and tagged his bill on the redistricting of Dallas." That was definitely the nuclear option! "I don't know or want to know who threw the first punch. But we need to get this settled. You can meet in my office."

I drove as fast as I could to the Capitol in Austin and arrived at the Speaker's office, or, as I thought of it at the moment, (the shootout at) the O.K. Corral.

I had called some of the Texas wine activists to update them. Ed Auler, who lived in Austin, was already there. Speaker Billy Clayton was there. I'm not sure but I think both Senator Harris and Representative Wilson had been told to stay far, far away, and away from each other as well. Butch Sparks was there, and the plan was for he and I to come to some kind of compromise on the bill. This is where they usually gutted your legislation if at all possible and if you weren't ready, it could be quick as a throat slit from behind, leaving you blinking and wondering what had just happened.

"First," I asked him, "just what is it you don't like about the bill?"

Butch looked at me like I had just asked him a pretty stupid question.

"I haven't read the bill," he said matter-of-factly.

"Then how do you know what it is you don't like?" I asked.

"We don't like change," he answered. "Any change."

I see.

"Well, change is a'coming so let's work it out," I said.

"What is it you want?"

I had taken each element of the bill, for example, the amount of grapes that might need to be imported, and added 25% to it, then asked for that figure. I did that for each provision of the bill and presented it to Butch.

He studied each provision, subtracted 25% from it, bringing the provisions back to what we really wanted to begin with—and he told me that's what he would allow.

"Gee," I said with false hesitation, then "Okay, we'll go for that."

After months of constant struggle, not to mention years of research and stake-holder education-building grassroots support, we had our wine bill. The rest was formalities.

It was a historic moment.

To be clear, there were no other Texas wine growers in the room or involved in the process, other than our hastily conceived and organized Texas Grape Growers cheering us on at pivotal moments. No one else put in long hours, or, in fact, any hours at the Capitol or contributed to our legislative costs. They were certainly offered the opportunity, but none contributed a dollar or a dime. It is said that success has many fathers and failure is an orphan. I'm aware of several Texas winemakers who claim responsibility for getting this historic legislation passed. It makes me think again of the St. Crispin's Day exhortation; those who lacked the will to take on this battle, who left the field and left the fight to others, when, years later, the actual warriors showed their scars from battle, would feel themselves unlucky not to have been there and fought for this great victory. I don't fault anyone for not being there, particularly as success was considered such a long shot, and ultimately, doing business in the future, each of us would have to deal with the liquor industry, one way or another. However, I do ask that each of them not claim ownership of an event they chose to stay a safe distance away from. It is perfectly okay to applaud a victory and participate in its rewards, without having to claim ownership of it.

But that's not to say this wasn't a shared effort.

Without Leon Adams and Pike Powers, there would not have been a Farm Winery Bill that became Texas law, enabling what would become a multibillion-dollar wine industry. Without the legislative team and Frank Tejeda, and particularly without the quick thinking and combative John Wilson, we would not have gotten the bill across the finish line. In the previous one hundred years, no one had been able to achieve this. On behalf of all wine growers and wine lovers in Texas, I would like to thank them all. And I hope this record puts them where they should be, in the history books that record the birth of the multibillion-dollar commercial wine industry in Texas.

After this historic victory, my communications team threw a celebration for me, with wine from Texas-grown grapes toasting the new Texas law and the newly empowered Texas wine industry. They presented me with a gavel, with a silver band engraved with "Gretchen's Wine Press," meant to acknowledge that we had not only pressed grapes, we had pressed the opposition to the mat and walked away victorious.

Shortly afterward, in June 1979, The Knights of the Vine, a prestigious wine society, held a major assemblage in Fort Worth, Texas, and inducted me into Knights of the Vine as Gentle Lady of the Vine, honoring my service to and promotion of the wine industry. My friend and ally, Dr. Bobby Smith, accompanied me to give me his blessings, along with that of the hundreds of other assembled members of this elite brother- and sisterhood, an organization whose roots went back to the 13th century.

The wine media also kindly acknowledged our historic victory:

Wine Spectator, July 1-15, 1979:

Despite archaic laws and overwhelming grass roots support for a native Texas wine industry, no one before Ms. Glasscock has been able to successfully sponsor legislation updating these laws.

The Wine Investor, June 18, 1979:

Grower Gretchen Glasscock, over opposition from spirits and retailer lobbies, got the Lone Star State's House and Senate to approve retail sales at wineries and 26 other changes in wine laws … So WINV raises its glass … and tips its 10-gallon Stetson to Ms. Glasscock.

_____

CHAPTER SIX

Starting Down the Road to Develop Texas Wineries

Texas' Many Large and Small Wineries

L ooking back, with the passage of the Texas Farm Winery Act in 1979, the Texas wine industry finally had a fighting chance. Although the infrastructure for a Texas wine industry was close to zero at that time, at least the seeds for success were sown. All we had to do was nurture and grow them, as we were nurturing and growing our vineyards.

The next step, for those rugged individualists who had taken huge bets and started vineyards, was to find a home for their grapes by supporting the creation of wineries to accept and process those grapes into wine.

Ste. Genevieve and the Power of the University of Texas

It is almost impossible to overstate the impact of the University of Texas' interest in pursuing the vineyard and wine business on its hundreds of thousands of acres of land in West Texas.

The rest of us were innovators, small growers with tiny vineyards, hoping, initially, to set up boutique wineries. The University of Texas, with its vast West Texas lands and almost bottomless deep pockets, along with its stable of horticulturists, viticulturists, chemists and labs already on the payroll and ready to provide backup and support to an industry start-up, were perceived as serious players capable of having a serious financial impact on the wine industry.

Ultimately the UT Board of Regents put the vineyard and winery project out for bids and a fierce battle for what looked like a potentially very profitable land grab ensued, with wine partner suitors set to leverage off UT's over two million acres of West Texas land and deep pockets filled with oil money. That episode, how the bids came in, who the players were, how the bids were handled and who finally emerged victorious, is a story in itself and, ultimately, we hope to tell that as well.

It is no coincidence that Pat Prendergast, current owner and president of Ste. Genevieve Winery and Mesa Vineyards in West Texas, previously worked with Gallo's international operations and Gallo's European operation. Gallo and Ste. Genevieve share the DNA of a giant winery. Ste. Genevieve does produce some private label premium wines, and they source some grapes from Texas, but much comes from California, South Africa, Chile and France, which are blended with a small portion of Texas grapes. It is good, reliable, well-made and well-marketed wine.

The foundation of Ste. Genevieve winery is an American-French partnership that was established in the early eighties between the University of Texas System and University Lands Office; and Richard Gill, Richter investors and Domaine Cordier of Cordier Estates from the village of Fuissé, in the Mâconnais region of Burgundy, one of France's finest terroirs. This winery project alone, which later morphed into Ste. Genevieve Winery and Mesa Vineyards, gave Texas credibility and stature in the wine industry. Its size and scale caught winemakers' attention globally and made them take notice and, at the very least, consider the possibility that Texas could become a serious player in the industry.

In fact, Ste. Genevieve is a serious player, able to make serious business deals in this industry. They produce about 16 wines, many to go on the shelves of large grocery and liquor chains, others private labeled for grocery stores and restaurants. Like Gallo wines, Ste. Genevieve wines are well made, consistent, good quality, "everyday" wines. They have wide distribution, and are familiar to buyers and popular with consumers.

However, even if one does occasionally enjoy a Ste. Genevieve wine, one may still be looking for a broader palette of wines, or further romance, artistry or individuality in their making. One's wine-buying habits come down to why one is tasting wine to begin with. These reasons can vary, according to circumstance. One might not opt for the same wine for a beach picnic or tailgating party as one would for a candlelight dinner. There are everyday wines, and there are special occasion wines, purchased for a special birthday, anniversary or celebration. One might be willing to pay top dollar for these special occasion wines and enjoy them from time to time.

But in between those two extremes—uniform and reliable everyday wines, including the occasional wine bargain one may find, particularly at huge stores like Costco; and expensive, "work-of-art" fine wines—there is a range of interesting and unique wines worthy of discovery. Once in France, at a wine-making château that was hundreds of years old, the owner took several of us out through the vineyard, where he expressed this thought on the wine-making process: "Think about it" he said. "Over time, everything changes. The weather changes, the soil changes, the wine-making techniques and ingredients change. The only thing that does not change is the owner's concept of how the wine should taste. And that vision of quality and unique taste is able to remain constant in the midst of the change that swirls around it."

There are many different and unique wines out there, and, specifically, in Texas, expressing an individual terroir and the owner's unique vision. If you are like me, one of the great jobs of wine tasting is that of exploration and discovery of the many unique tastes and visions that our good earth, given the proper conditions and the artistry of a winemaker, can produce.

In fact, great winemaker André Tchelistcheff pointed out in Leon Adams's book, *The Wines of America*: "As the production of the leading vintners in Europe and America continues to grow in volume, their wines become more uniform; they have less opportunity to engage in pioneering experiments. … The apostolic mission of the future … belongs to the small wine grower."[16]

So let's all hail the pioneering small wine growers of Texas and the progress Texas and the rest of the United States have made in refining their wine taste and knowledge and the level of expertise that goes into wine making. Then let's take an educated look at Texas wine regions that produce specific types of wines with characteristics unique to that region.

---

16 Leon Adams, *The Wines of America*, 545.

Back in the late seventies, when I first began my serious study of wines, much of the U.S. was consuming Blue Nun, a somewhat sweet white German wine, or possibly even Mogen David, a Labrusca of very modest quality. At that time, I was educating all of us about vinifera varietals, the classic wine grapes of Europe and California: Chardonnay and Cabernet, for example. The changes since then have been enormous and, certainly for Texas, impactful.

Texas' Eight AVA Wine Regions and Suitable Varieties

Our successes include the development of the AVA or American Viticultural Area system in Texas, which allows viticulturists to better match the type of grape grown with the specific climate and terroir of the area in which it is planted. The move beyond the classic vinifera grapes, exemplified by Chardonnay and Cabernet, into experimentation with grape varieties that fare better in warmer weather such as Southern Europe, has allowed our vintners to expand their palette and begin creating wines uniquely suited to Texas and expressive of regional Texas terroirs.

During the latter part of the 1970s, we were using the degree-day system to define a region's suitability to produce wine because we hadn't yet created the AVA system, the officially designated wine-growing-area classification system that was not created until 1978. It was critically important to the viticulturist and winemaker to know and understand the exact climate conditions for which he or she was attempting to match a grape varietal that would have the most potential for quality. As André Tchelistcheff used to say: "Great wines are created in the vineyard."

In other words, despite the considerable artistry, skills and techniques of a great winemaker, one must start with a truly high-quality grape in order to produce a great wine. And a grape will only be high quality if it is not only managed correctly on the vine and during the growing and harvesting season, but placed, to begin with, in the climate and terroir that is best suited to its individual characteristics.

It was a big step forward for the Texas wine industry when Bob Oberhelman of the former incarnation of Bell Mountain Vineyards in Central Texas filed for an AVA for Bell Mountain, which was granted in 1986. This designation enabled the beginning of a more precise, detailed and scientific designation of wine regions in Texas.

Today, "Texas is home to eight American Viticultural Areas:[17]

- Mesilla Valley AVA (1985) - West Texas. Texas' first AVA though primarily located in New Mexico with only small parts extending into Texas.

- Bell Mountain AVA (1986) - Central Texas. First AVA completely within the state of Texas. Known for its distinctive Cabernet Sauvignon grown in northern Gillespie County.

- Fredericksburg in the Texas Hill Country AVA (1989) - Central Texas. Known for its Cabernet Sauvignon and Chardonnay.

- Texas Hill Country AVA (1991) - Central Texas. Located just west of Austin. With over 9,000,000 acres (3,600,000 ha), it is the second largest AVA in the United States, though less than 800 acres (320 ha) are planted in grape vines.

- Escondido Valley AVA (1992) - West Texas. About 32,000 acres (13,000 ha) along the Pecos River in Pecos County.

- Texas High Plains AVA (1993) - North Texas. About 85% of the wine grapes in Texas are grown on the Texas High Plains on approximately 4,000 acres (1,600 ha). The AVA is the second largest AVA with over 8,000,000 acres (3,200,000 ha). Elevation ranges from 3,300 to 3,700 feet.

- Texas Davis Mountains AVA (1998) - West TexasSpecializes in Cabernet Sauvignon and Sauvignon Blanc.

- Texoma AVA (2005) - North Texas. The Texoma region is where 19th-century viticulturist Thomas Volney Munson discovered the cure for France's phylloxera epidemic.

---

17 https://en.wikipedia.org/wiki/American_Viticultural_Area

According to WineBusiness.com: "Vineyards in Texas are located in five regions. The High Plains region grows 60% of the grapes in the state and includes two American Viticultural Areas (AVAs): the Texas High Plains AVA and Texoma AVA. The North Texas region near Dallas/Fort Worth has 60 wineries and 63 vineyards that are members of the Texas Wine Grape Growers Association, while the Gulf Coast region has 26 winery members. The Hill Country region west of Austin has 60 winery members in TWGGA and three AVAs: Bell Mountain AVA, Fredericksburg AVA and Texas Hill Country AVA. The oldest winery in Texas, Val Verde Winery which dates to 1883, is located in West Texas, a region with three AVAS: Escondido Valley AVA, Mesilla Valley AVA, and the Texas Davis Mountains AVA."[18]

It should be noted that grapes from the cooler growing regions of the High Plains and Davis Mountains AVAs are much sought after for their high quality in wine making. Many of the wineries in other areas bring in and use grapes from these AVAs for their premium wine production.

The Winery Imperative

Given the pivotal financial importance of having one's own winery to maximize the value of one's grapes, and to avoid some of the vagaries of the market—with grapes, like all commodities, being subject to wide price swings, in addition to being held hostage to unpredictable weather—I definitely intended to develop a winery.

A well-outfitted winery, particularly one of a certain scale, is very expensive. The best winemakers want to work in only the best wineries with the most expensive equipment. I was already working, somewhat nonstop, on other family business just to keep my head above water and meet the payroll at the vineyard, for both employees and consultants. With no Texas banks loaning on vineyards, I was in a bit of a quandary about how I could raise sufficient money to construct a quality winery.

Imagine my relief, then, at hearing from an acquaintance from Fort Worth, who worked at the U.S. Department of Agriculture, that their Rural Development area

18 https://www.winebusiness.com/news/?go=getArticle&dataId=212655

had been watching and discussing my progress with the vineyard and wine development, and they had agreed they wanted to provide me with a $2 million grant. (Two million dollars in 1978 would be $8.15 million in 2020. It could certainly pay for a winery.)

The USDA, with the goal of providing financial and technical assistance for struggling rural areas, was prioritizing towns with fewer than 20,000 residents. All of Jeff Davis County at that time had less than 20,000 people. In fact, the entire county had less than 1,600 people, and in 2020 still has less than 2,600. Boy, did we qualify!

I was really excited and energized by this wonderful revelation. The only catch was that I had to apply locally and have the application go up through the normal channels. When it reached the regional office in Fort Worth, it would be approved. That much was a given.

Applying for a USDA Grant as a Woman in West Texas

I set out to get my application into the local office, which was in Fort Stockton. Fort Stockton is not very affluent, with an economy based on sheep and cattle ranching and the occasional boom and bust of an oil strike. Like most small, rural, agricultural towns, many there had been raised on farms or ranches, and the dream of working on one was always with them.

I tried for weeks to get an appointment with the area director of Fort Stockton's Rural Development Service Center Office. I'll call him John Park (not his real name). I had no success whatever. I just could not get an appointment. Since this lack of an appointment was standing between me and $2 million to construct a winery, I developed an alternate plan. I would just drop by. It wasn't really that casual a drop-in, because Fort Stockton was about an hour-and-a-half drive from Fort Davis. I would also wait until near closing time, to assure Mr. Park would not be tied up in meetings.

And that is what I did. I drove over and walked into the office, shortly before it closed, and, as luck would have it, only Mr. Park was there, alone.

"Mr. Park," I said, "so glad to see you. I don't think we've met. I'm Gretchen Glasscock. I've been trying to set up an appointment with you for some time so I just thought I'd drop by. I won't take but a minute of your time. I just wanted to drop by an application."

John Park looked at me like he had just spotted a rattlesnake or a tarantula in his boot. "I know who you are," he said in a pretty surly way.

"Well then," I said, "you probably know why I'm here. I'm interested in applying for a Rural Development grant so I can continue developing a business in Fort Davis, but one that is good for this entire region."

Mr. Park gave me a withering stare. "If there is anything I hate, it's rich people from Houston who decide to come here and set up in this part of the country," he said.

"I'm from San Antonio," I pointed out. I could have pointed out that, after all the investments I'd made in West Texas, I was anything but rich. If I were rich, I wouldn't need a grant to build a winery. But I got his drift. There were many cowboys all over Texas or, at least, men dressed like cowboys, who wanted nothing more than to make a living off a farm or ranch and were seriously ticked off that they weren't able to do it. "People from Houston" was somewhat of a metaphor they used for very wealthy people who came to West Texas and bought an expensive spread, but, in their view, weren't real cowboys. As it happened, I had been running 20,000 acres of ranchland for a number of years, so, in that respect, I imagined I was about as much of a "cowboy" as he was. But, of course, that argument wasn't going to fly, so I just listened.

"Let me spell it out for you," John Park said with thinly disguised hostility. "I would like to be working on a farm. But I can't make a living and feed my family that way. Instead, I work at the drugstore and here. I am sure not going to give you money so you can operate a vineyard and build a winery."

This seemed a little self-defeating to me, because if he wanted to, he could work there. But I got it. He didn't want me doing it.

"I am not going to give you the money or help you get the money. In fact, I'm going to make it my business to see that you *never* get that money."

Well, that was a real punch in the gut.

I sort of nodded and backed out the door. I certainly didn't want him getting more worked up than he already was.

All was not lost, I reasoned. There was another Rural Development Office in El Paso. I figured El Paso, being a bit larger town, might be a little more welcoming to newcomers than Mr. Park was.

El Paso was about three hours from Fort Davis. I made plans to go there the next day. There was a lot of empty land between Fort Davis and El Paso, so it was not a fun or interesting drive. Going anyplace in West Texas requires navigating long stretches of remote area. But I had my goal firmly in mind, so I soldiered on.

When I arrived at the Rural Development Office in El Paso and walked through the door, who should be sitting in the office waiting room but John Park? He looked at me and smiled, but not in a kind way. He had come to shut down my dream.

And he did. That was my best hope for a winery, and it was off the table.

Actually, there was a lot more going on in this dynamic and this interaction than just a question of whether I, personally, would get a winery development grant. There was a lot to unpack here.

First, I thought this was unfortunate, not just for me, but for the economy of Jeff Davis County, for the Texas wine industry and, arguably, Texas agribusiness in general. Turning one's back on this development assistance for Jeff Davis County also meant turning one's back on a long-stunted area of Texas, which was not enjoying any of the vibrancy and growth benefits so many other areas of the state had seen on a continuous basis. Desolate was one way to describe the area. Underpopulated was another. Yes, it was very beautiful, even majestic, but that did not put food on one's table. The fact is, at this time, the county was on a continuous decline propped up only by some government properties, a very few hangers-on and a handful of wealthy people from other areas who sought refuge in the remote mountains. Lacking other outlets, particularly for young men without much access to good-paying jobs, it also gave rise, occasionally, to some pretty far-out groups. One example is those who believed in the "Republic of Texas," deciding that Texas hadn't been legally annexed by the United States but was still an independent nation, owed huge sums in reparations by the United States. As much of a stir as their antics caused at the time, including a much-publicized armed standoff with law enforcement, they were only a temporary blip in the normally peaceful and serene existence in Fort Davis.

I didn't understand many of the dynamics at play at that time. It wasn't until much later that books began to explore the disadvantages felt by white, working-class men, particularly in rural areas, and the extreme resentment they felt about it. Other dynamics were at play as well. When small towns begin to experience growth, it is not uncommon, particularly in the beginning, for friction to arise between locals and newcomers, often perceived to be interlopers. And there also is the question of what is the women's role in the economic side of society, apart from hearth and home. It was not until November of 1995 that the U.S. Department of Labor put out the "Glass Ceiling Report," which gave rise to the term or metaphor of "a glass ceiling," beyond which women could not rise.

It starts with a gender pay gap with which most of us, at least most women, are entirely familiar.

Since that time, an entire body of research has developed, regarding women's historic disadvantage in the workplace, compared to men, and new concepts have been defined and articulated to describe what happens as women try to climb the career ladder or succeed as entrepreneurs. In fact, later on, in the mid-1990s, shortly after Netscape came out with the browser opening up the commercial web, I created one of the first women's websites to address this issue. AdvancingWomen.com set out to level the playing field for women in careers. The problem was particularly acute in male-dominated fields like engineering, technology, construction and agri-business. Women, globally, were impacted by this phenomenon and so anxious to find and communicate with other women about it that the first month I launched the site it had four million visitors and crashed the server three times.

Back in the 1970s, I didn't understand this although I had sensed inklings of it. Friends' mothers expected the son in the family to take over the family business, and it was perfectly okay for the daughter, even if she had graduated from Columbia, to work behind the counter of an art gallery or bookstore, a refined and genteel profession. I'm not sure fathers of that era thought about this at all, since, after sending daughters to the right schools and joining the right clubs, they expected daughters to get married, preferably well. Aside from my own father's constant total support and mentoring, to some extent, I also had been in a bubble where old ranching families were a bit protective of me, as a daughter of one of their own who had fallen. I hadn't been exposed to this level of animosity in business, or, in fact, anything but extreme politeness and gracious acceptance.

In effect, if John Park, Rural Development Officer for the USDA in Fort Stockton, had been equally qualified for a winery development grant to open a new industry in the qualifying area of Fort Davis, he would have received it, with few questions asked. A woman who qualified for it would not, despite the more progressive atti-tudes of the Board in Fort Worth; in fact, she would not have even been able to submit an application that would get her in the pipeline for consideration. John Park was very clear on that point. He was never, ever going to allow my application for a winery development grant to be submitted. My application was never going to reach Fort Worth to be approved because it was never going to be submitted. Since I am not a mind reader, it was impossible for me to know whether John Park's extreme agitation with me was because he saw me as a rich "interloper" from Houston, as he had pointed out, or simply an intrinsically undeserving woman, or some toxic combination of both. One can't even be sure he knew himself, although I'm sure he knew he saw "red" every time my face popped up. In any case, it was a moot point. The practical effect was my hope for financing for a winery had hit a wall.

A Big Decision

The time had come for me to make a decision. Was I going to continue to pursue financing for construction of my own winery? I was pretty much out on a limb already with the investments I had put into the land, the vineyard, the wine expertise and the passage of the wine legislation to benefit all Texas vineyard and winery owners. (This was despite being advised by some mentors never to do anything to benefit the entire industry, who were, after all, potential competitors. Only under-take initiatives to benefit yourself and your own business. I got it. But it seemed pretty much of a conundrum to me. One needed to have a viable industry first, then tend to one's own competitive needs. In any case, I didn't take the advice to let someone else grow corn or sorghum on my land and send me a check for the profits, which, from a business standpoint, was very sound. It just didn't resonate with my temperament. I wanted to be part of creating the future, and developing a vineyard was my ticket to doing that.

I already had sold some property to make what, for me, were large investments in this very early stage wine industry. Was I going to continue to cannibalize an ongoing business from which my family derived its living? I really had to struggle with this tough decision. I had to sort through my own dreams and ambitions, as opposed to the practical needs of my own family and myself. In the end, I thought back to my poker rules. One had to know when to hold 'em and when to fold 'em. I decided not to gamble any further income at this stage. I would proceed on and, perhaps, at a later stage of development in the Texas wine industry, when I was better positioned, I would jump back into a more robust participation, in whatever form that might take. That would be the intent of the next phase of the business that I will be discussing: AdvancingTexasWine.com, an online wine sales site.

Hiatus

It was at this point that I decided to take a break from the pressures and challenges of the nascent Texas wine business.

At our Blue Mountain Vineyard, we had installed a metal frame building with a small office, a tiny lab and some stainless steel tanks. So, yes, we were able to experiment in making wine. But that scale of winery was not going to attract and support the best winemakers. It certainly could support small DIY and experimental winemakers, and no one can deny the possibility that the wine made there potentially could compete with the best. But it was not what I envisioned for myself and not what I wanted to pursue.

In the first place, I was not a winemaker but an entrepreneur. I was in business and wanted to create a certain scale of business that would be not only sustainable for myself but would support others, preferably the best in their fields. This was not in the cards for a large closet-sized lab and a few stainless steel tanks. So I stepped away from active, business participation in the Texas wine business for a time.

One of the first tasks facing me was that I needed to shore up my depleted resources. That wasn't going to happen anytime soon in the early stage Texas wine business. Unfortunately, the oil business in Texas had been languishing at that time as well. My family had some property in Live Oak County that I had offered to lease to just about anyone in the Texas oil business able to pay for a lease. No takers. The only person remotely interested in this property, for about a five-year period, was one sole geologist who saw something in his charts and graphs that he thought very exciting. He repeatedly offered me $5,000 for a long-term lease. I explained to him, repeatedly, that I would love to accept $5,000 for it, that $5,000 would mean a lot to me at that moment, but that if I accepted that offer, I couldn't take another. In other words, I would be cutting off all potential for a big payday, which I needed at that point. Like many in the oil business, I relied on those scarce, roll-of-the-dice big paydays to compensate for all the lean times and, hopefully, set me up for whatever was to come next.

As luck would have it, about this time, a tiny foreshadowing of what was to become the Austin Chalk-Eagle Ford Shale play began to heat up. Austin Chalk is a geological formation with similar characteristics stretching across fields in Texas, Louisiana and into Mississippi. The discovery of such a formation, when it coincided with the technology to extract the oil or gas economically, signaled the birth of a boom. What would become clusters of producing wells were known by the name of the formation—the Austin Chalk play.

Luckily, some of the Austin Chalk formation was on our property. As landowners, if we signed a lease, we got a bonus, then received royalties from the production, if any. Now, suddenly, the Live Oak property was in demand. The first I heard of it was when an oil landman knocked on my door and wanted to lease it. A big sigh of relief washed over me. I gave him my word he could have it. That's how business was done on a certain level in those days. My word was my bond. Period.

Later, on our way into a courthouse to complete the transaction with my lawyer and the landman, a complete stranger, another landman—or, in this case a woman—from another company suddenly approached us, as if she'd been lying in wait. She began making excited, higher offers for the Live Oak property. My lawyer, I regret to report, turned to me and said: "You go wait around the corner. I will handle this." I promptly responded: "You're the hired gun here. You go wait around the corner and I will settle it."

So much for respecting your employer. Amazing what surfaces in times of stress.

Finally, the new oil company bidder made a considerably higher offer. I turned to the first landman and said: "Let's step aside for a moment and talk alone."

We moved down the hall for some privacy and he said, with considerable consternation: "That's my limit. I'm not allowed to go higher."

"Okay," I said. "I'm going to give it to you. But I have a smaller lease coming up in a few months and I'd like for you to take it as well, so I won't be criticized by my family for taking less."

"I'll sign up for it now," he said.

"Then it's a done deal."

My soon-to-be ex-lawyer and the new oil company bidder were flabbergasted that I had taken a slightly lesser offer. But I had kept my word, which was an iron-clad rule, particularly when most of your business was done on the phone. And the offer, after all, was six figures. Enough to pay off my debts. I was in the game again.

Pioneering on the Net

During this time, the University of Texas at San Antonio Business Department asked me if I would review and fine tune some research for them and write a paper to support it. They had collected anecdotal stories that seemed to suggest women business owners earned less than men business owners. This was before the glass ceiling report came out and confirmed this discrepancy in earnings. I agreed, and what they handed me was a box of clippings from various newspapers and magazines. In fact, at the end of this process, they gave me a payment just for the research I did, because they certainly hadn't done any, aside from their box of newspaper clippings.

It was about the same time, or shortly after, that Netscape came out with the first commercial browser. Before that time, the Net appeared in default gray background and blue text with no graphics. It was populated with researchers, engineers, scientists and government workers. There definitely was no WOW! Factor—more like a Snooze factor.

Nonetheless, I was fascinated by the potential. I started thinking of putting the two together, the research on women and the Net, which was becoming enlivened by the Netscape browser, now open to ordinary citizens, although no commercial ventures were on it yet. In other words, there was zero competition. It definitely was a new frontier, and that's where I preferred to hang out, win, lose or draw.

I began where I usually begin, at square one. There was no "What You See Is What You Get" (WYSIWYG) software, so I taught myself HTML coding. When

I got stuck, a group of tech women in Silicon Valley came to my rescue, for which I was and still am grateful. One woman tech, who was invaluable to me was Roan Bear, an outstanding and generous professional whose advice saved me many times.

I was fortunate because, with no commercial competition and, really, not much to do yet on the Net, my first website—AdvancingWomen.com—had four million visitors the first month and crashed the server three times. A global audience of women was hungry for the kind of information AdvancingWomen.com offered. We explained to women how to use the new tools on the Net to reach out, network, get a mentor, balance work and family and keep moving up the ladder. Over time, I cofounded the "Advancing Women in Leadership Journal," the first online professional, refereed journal for women in leadership. I developed, executed and advised the strategic direction for websites for professional and business organizations, universities and software developers in the U.S. & Europe. My website won Lycos's Top 5% award and a Dow Jones award, and was rated a Beatrice-Yahoo Top Site and WWWomen Best of Net. It was listed in Femina as a top women's career site and featured in *Elle, Self, Women and Success*, and *Fast Company* magazines; *Access*, a Sunday supplement; *Business Class*, an Australian magazine; and *the San Antonio Business Journal.*

I attended an Internet conference in Tampa with 5,000 men and five women and Tim Berners-Lee, who is credited with "inventing" the Internet, or at least making it useable by ordinary citizens.

I was invited to the White House to discuss women's issues globally, and participated in conferences, including in Brussels, to train businesswomen how to leverage technology.

Eventually, I was doing business in about 12 of the 24 time zones on Earth. At the same time, I was financial news editor for MoneyMinded.com, an offshoot of Hearst's Women.com, the largest website geared to women on the Net.

I loved what I was doing, the life I was living and the people I was meeting. But, eventually, the time came to return home.

CHAPTER SEVEN

Coming Home to a Significantly Advanced Wine Industry

Retrospective: Development of the Texas Wine and Grape Growers Association – Collaboration and Institutionalized Knowledge

One of the critical advances achieved by the industry during my absence was the development of institutionalized knowledge, information and practices by a group representing the industry. The Texas Wine and Grape Growers Association, you will recall, was just a name that a handful of us wine activists gave ourselves as we were trying to get the Farm Winery Act passed. In the beginning there were no bylaws, board of directors or committees, just a couple of us talking on the phone when something came up or putting out a congratulatory statement when we made any progress. Today there are committees that study the issues, analyze them and help develop policies to address them.

This group definitely has been responsible for much of the progress that has been made in the Texas wine industry.

In the ensuing years, the Texas wine industry has had many successes and some elusive and lingering challenges as well as brand-new, daunting challenges—like the advent of the coronavirus and the off-and-on shutdown of wine-tasting rooms and wine tasting festivals, on which the industry sales are largely dependent.

A Wine Region on the Cusp

According to an April 25, 2019, article *in Wine Spectator*, one of the bibles of the wine industry: "There's a lot of potential in Texas and a lot of work has already been done, but there's still a ways to go. 'This is Napa in the late sixties,' [Benjamin] Calais [of Calais Winery] said.

"In the meantime, get yourself out there to experience this up-and-coming region. Maybe 20 years from now, you'll be telling your friends you were drinking Texas wine before it was cool … or cult."[19]

Texas Wines Achieve Award-winning Status

In 1986, Llano Estacado Winery won a Double Gold award at the San Francisco Fair wine competition, marking a turning point for the prestige and acceptance of Texas wine at the highest levels and among the most august competitors. The results of subsequent wine competitions as well as the 2020 San Francisco Chronicle Wine Competition and various other international wine tastings confirm that Texas premier wines, when well selected, particularly from a unique terroir, can go up against the best wines from any region.

What does this mean for Texas?

---

19 https://www.winespectator.com/articles/future-is-bright-for-texas-wine

Texas Wine Industry's Economic Impact on Texas

In 2017, the Economic Impact Study on wine brought some very good news. According to the Texas Wine and Grape Growers Association's interpretation of the report:

The production, distribution, sales, and consumption of wine in Texas benefits many sectors of the state's economy and **generates close to $13.1 billion in total economic activity**. This ultimate value-added product preserves agricultural land, provides American jobs, attracts tourists, generates taxes, and enhances the quality of life.

State Reach: The Texas wine industry includes a total of 394 wine producers as well as 4,368 acres of vineyards.

Job Creation: The Texas wine industry directly employs as many as 60,716 people, and generates an additional 16,949 jobs in supplier and ancillary industries which supply goods and services to the industry, and whose sales depend on the wine industry's economic activity. Ultimately, 104,627 jobs are created and supported by the wine industry.

Wage Generation: The Texas wine industry provides good jobs, paying an average of $41,400 in annual wages and benefits. The total wages generated by direct, indirect, and induced economic activity driven by the wine industry are $4.3 billion."[20]

---

20 https://www.txwines.org/texas-report/..

CRITICAL ADVANCES

Legislation

2001 – The Texas Legislature creates the Texas Wine Marketing Assistance Program.

2005 – The Texas Legislature approves a bill allowing wineries to ship their wines anywhere in the state.

Legislation regarding labeling of Texas wines has been introduced several times without moving out of committee. Apparently opinion is split among two groups, those who feel the current requirement of 75% Texas grapes and finishing in Texas is a solid standard. And those on the other side, who are fighting for a designation of 100% Texas grapes as a labeling requirement. One side believes that dealing with weather setbacks and other issues require the flexibility of using juice from other regions. The other side points to regions like Bordeaux and Champagne and insist that recognition for quality comes with these stricter standards. To some extent, this comes down to an argument between perfectionism and economics. Most of the larger wineries believe it is vital to have the flexibility to supplement supply in bad seasons, with out-of-state juice, which is a very practical viewpoint.

Financing

Again, the growth of the wine industries, like other industries, is tied to the availability of capital investment, the money patterns that allow the wine industry to be an attractive investment. The financing options that are available at every stage of the process, from planting to harvesting, to aging and sales are key to growing the industry. Heritage Land Bank, for one, offers wine industry financing across a broad spectrum, from land purchases to infrastructure, including building and facilities, to harvesting and processing equipment to starting new operations or expanding existing ones. This is invaluable assistance for the creation, maintenance and expansion of an industry.

Education

At the birth of the contemporary wine industry, if one wanted to enroll in academic studies to pursue a card in the wine industry, one had to go to U.C. Davis or a similar out-of-state university. Now there are an increasing number of options to get a certification or a degree in plant and soil science, viticulture or winemaking from universities like Texas A & M, Texas Tech and Palo Alto College in the Alamo Colleges District.

Processing

Now Texas has full support for enology, providing key tannins, enzymes and yeasts for the tailored fermentation of wines.

Growing and Harvesting

Today Texas has a full range of suppliers in all types of vineyard and winery equipment as well as specialists in irrigation and landscape supply. In addition, there are specialists that bring in "capable, reliable, legal labor" under H-2A services, meaning access to workers with extensive experience in just this kind of vineyard work.

Custom Crush Winery

There is now a Custom Crush winery, Sage's Vintage, that provides a customized and tailored experience for wineries, offering crush services, bottling, wine production and complete winery planning. Having a Custom Crush winery is a valuable option in the industry growth process, allowing a grower options. It's no longer necessary for a wine grower to finance and construct his or her own winery. Winemakers can use this facility and, if they choose, be enabled to grow their wine organizations at their own pace and, if desired, ultimately construct their own wineries without pressure.

Advanced Wine Technology

Innovations like GOfermentor™ expand the crush and fermentation possibilities for small wineries. "The GOfermentor is a patented automated wine making system that ferments in single use liners."[21] These are compact units requiring 48x48 inches of floor space and a pallet jack or forklift to move it, and standard, household 110 electric service. GOfermentor also provides "SmartBarrel" to "store your win without oxidation," no topping or cleaning required. You can also partially fill these barrels without threat of oxidation. Anything that gives a winemaker options, in terms of size or ease of use, is helpful in growing the industry.

Wine Software

Today there is winery management software enabling "bud to bottle" management of every aspect of one's wine product.

Marketing Support

Photography, video, graphic design for labeling, digital media management and event support for the vineyard and wine industry are now available commercially.

AdvancingTexasWine.com will supply an online sales portal for Texas wineries, eliminating the need for online

21 https://www.gofermentor.com/advanced-winemaking/

tech skills to continuously educate the public, increase outreach and manually update product information and pricing.

Struggle for Diversity and Inclusion

Only recently have women in the Texas wine industry, many of whom have outstanding credentials or accomplishments, come to be recognized. "Grape Dames, Some of the Hill Country's Women in Wine,"[22] published in *Rock & Vine*, details some of these women, including Susan Auler of Fall Creek Vineyards. Also, one would have to acknowledge Merrill Bonarrigo, a cofounder of Messina Hof Winery in Bryan, Texas, and a force within the industry.

Other women in the Texas wine scene were recognized in a July 26, 2019, article in Texas Tech University's "The Agriculturist," showcasing "West Texas Wine Women" including Katy Jane Seaton, who, along with her husband, his sister and brother-in-law, owns Farmhouse Vineyards in Meadow, Texas.

The *Wall Street Journal's* Lettie Teague, who writes about wine, reports that black women often feel unwelcome in the industry and that some industry organizations like Court of Master Sommeliers display bias against women and particularly black women. With some of their instructors insisting students address them as "Master," a term loaded with negative and hurtful associations, not surprisingly some women feel discrimination does, indeed, exist in the industry.[23]

Lia Jones, a black woman with stellar sommelier credentials, applied for 76 wine jobs in New York in 2015-16 and never got one. In 2018, she founded Diversity in Wine and Spirits, a nonprofit advocacy group, and she serves as executive director, attempting to create a more equitable environment for women of color in the worlds of wine and restaurants. She works with industry groups like the International Wine Center, whose tagline is "fostering wine and spirits education since 1982."

We certainly join in this effort to "level the playing field" for women of color in the wine industry.

22 https://rockandvinemag.com/2019/08/grape-dames/

23 https://www.wsj.com/articles/for-black-women-in-wine-the-industry-has-been-inhospitable-11597744839

All of these factors—the development of recognized AVAs, the broadening of wine varieties that have proven successful in unique Texas terroir, the growth of both vineyards and wineries and all aspects of the economic impact of Texas wine—are big successes for the Texas wine industry.

We do have some areas, however, that present challenges for the industry, some of them daunting.

One such challenge is that Texas four to six thousand acres of vineyards simply are not enough to support the burgeoning Texas wine industry. In fact, most of our wine is sourced outside of Texas. Planting and growing a vineyard is a cash-intensive business, requiring $10,000 an acre or more and waiting three to five years before the vines will produce grapes. That is one problem to be addressed. One solution might be an exploration of ways to develop more support from the state, particularly since the state itself, in the form of the UT System Permanent University Fund, and its 2.1 million acres across 19 counties in West Texas, is a partner in the largest winery in Texas: Ste. Genevieve, which we have discussed at length earlier. This is a one of the largest wineries in the United States, easily the largest winery in Texas. It dominates the market and sells more than half of Texas wine. Considering the multibillion-dollar impact of the Texas wine industry, and the profits flowing into UT's coffers, a program to contribute to vineyard development to benefit not only Texas wine growers but Texas taxpayers seems like one reasonable option.

But there is another, more pressing challenge: Covid-19 and its devastating impact on the Texas wine industry.

Coming Home – the Texas Wine Scene Today

I had always thought someday I might reenter the Texas wine business. But it was always more like those dreamy "what if" sequences you run through your head, without much thought of how or when or if you would actually follow up on them.

Then, one evening, through mutual friends, I met Dacota Haselwood, an engaging and knowledgable professional who was executive director of the Texas Grape

Growers Association. Tasting some Texas wine she had brought, around an island in the kitchen of a stately home in Monte Vista, San Antonio, we began to reminisce about the Texas wine industry. She caught me up to date with a lot of developments, including the fact that the best grapes, from the cooler regions I had identified, were used in the finest Texas wines. I also learned no one had ever heard of the study Ron Perry of Texas A & M had produced, stating that all Texas was a Region V, the hottest region.

"They probably burned it," I commented, mostly in jest. Still, it was the beginning of my realization of how little was known or had been recorded about those early days of the birth of the contemporary Texas wine industry.

Sometime later, I happened to run into Lionel Sosa, the architect of my communication strategy that laid the groundwork for the passage of the historic farm winery legislation.

"That was historic," he said. "That was a turning point in what has become a major multibillion industry in our state."

It was beginning to look like someone should actually record that history before it was lost in the mists of time.

Also, as I began paying attention, I noticed that at least two men had claimed responsibility for the passage of the Farm Winery Bill, even though neither of them had even been present, or worked to achieve it, beyond a round of applause from a safe and inexpensive distance. During this ordeal, which they observed from the sidelines and now sought to claim credit for, my legislative team and I worked often around the clock, were subjected to constant intimidation and hostility and were forced to wield a machete through the thick jungle of obstacles we faced.

And that is when I began thinking of reengaging with the Texas wine scene and possibly recording the seeds of its modern beginning. I felt a real need to set the record straight.

I started off with asking a group of friends over for a tasting of fine Texas wines at my home. I was very impressed with the quality they had achieved.

Next, I began to catch up with the developments in the Texas wine scene.

44th Annual Texas Wine and Grape Growers Association Conference and Trade Show

To further educate myself, I decided in February 2020 to attend the 44th Annual Texas Wine and Grape Growers Association Conference and Trade Show in Irving. This beautiful powerhouse of a city just outside Dallas has a concentration of restaurants and amenities and a gorgeous, very contemporary convention center. Irving itself is famous for its striking bronze sculpture by Robert Glen of nine wild horses galloping through water.

Although at the time we had no idea of the extent of the deadly impact of Covid-19, I didn't feel comfortable getting on a plane, so we, Carla A. Salinas, my spouse, and I, decided to make the four-hour drive by car. We arrived and stayed at the very lovely and well-located Omni Mandalay at Las Colinas. From start to end, this was not your father's grape growers' conference; this was plush. And, if you weren't getting all your needs, particularly your sensory needs, met, you must have been asleep or somewhere else. Of course there were all the educational vineyard and winery tracks, with a good number of Texas A & M or Texas AgriLife Extension Service professors. But there were also sales tracks with expert wine industry professionals, social media tracks with high level marketing professionals and technologists, and business tracks with top law firms and with specialists in local and federal legislation and regulation. If you wanted to learn, you were in the right place.

At the Industry Celebration and Gala, you could forget your dusty plains and high noon rustic simplicity. Items were farm-to-market fresh and locally sourced, and the presentation and preparation were strictly five star. The selection of wines for each course was, heart-stoppingly superb. In a mere few decades, Texas, at least those in the state who cared about fine wine and food and were building a local industry, had lifted its cuisine from hearty country food to a level that could compare with any elevated gastronomy in any country or region.

After splitting up and participating in many of the most interesting and informative tracks, I, accompanied by Carla A. Salinas, who had joined me on the trip, went to the ballroom for the Celebration and Gala. Dacota Hazelwood had seated us at a table in front with engaging winery founders, the Messina Hoff clan: Paul Bonarrigo; his very accomplished wife, Merrill; and their son, Paul Mitchell Bonarrigo, and wife, Karen, who are now running the winery. The Bonarrigo family pioneered the wine industry in Texas; they are influential and high profile as well as being personable and charming. They now have wineries at three locations with multiple hospitality venues and are constructing a fourth location just outside Houston, a huge market. We thoroughly enjoyed our visit with them and the other winemakers who came up to greet us.

Paul got up to speak and he graciously recognized my history in the industry and passage of the historic Farm Winery Act. I also posed afterward with some young women who had just succeeded in passing new legislation to further advance the industry.

With all the tracks and trade shows, we walked away with some new knowledge of developments in the Texas wine industry. When we departed the conference it was with high spirits and renewed enthusiasm for the bright future of this wonderful industry that brought joy and purpose to so many. We did not see the enormous magnitude of the storm clouds that were gathering for these and so many other industries.

CHAPTER EIGHT

Covid-19 and the Online Wine Sales Imperative

A Critical Turning Point for the Texas Wine Industry

O nce again, the Texas wine industry finds itself at a crucial turning point in its survival and future success. The Covid-19 shutdowns and impact have created a crisis for the Texas wine industry, like many other industries. But crisis also represents opportunity. Perhaps Shakespeare's Julius Caesar said it best: There is a tide in the affairs of men, which, taken at the flood, leads on to fortune; (not seized), all the voyage of their life is bound in shallows and in miseries."

This time of crisis is our opportunity to seize the moment and create a wine sales platform that will assure the survival of even the smallest of our beloved Texas wineries with their emphasis on individualized wines and earth-friendly practices.

Just as in the St. Crispin's Day speech, when King Henry V urged his men on to battle, those who join this bold effort and take on this good fight will be remembered with honor; their names and reputations will be recalled in many annals recording the successful arc of the Texas wine industry. Who wouldn't aspire to that?

As the Texas wine industry has evolved, as far as sales and revenue are concerned, it has developed a tourist and entertainment business model. The first sales point is the winery tasting room, where the owner can keep not only the producer, but also the wholesale and retail share of the profits. In addition, perhaps 20% of sales are of wine paraphernalia, like glasses, corkscrews, T-shirts, caps, books, guides and whatever. Doubling down on this model, many wineries have installed restaurants, private tasting rooms, bed and breakfast guest houses and hospitality upgrades such as wedding, celebration and meeting venues. In addition, Texas has had roughly 140 wine festivals a year, each attracting thousands of visitors before the Covid-19 shutdown. All of these are hospitality or entertainment venues, so, instead of providing diversification, enabling a winery to weather an economic storm, the reliance on them has increased the exposure of many wineries to the current adverse conditions. Overhead and payroll has increased without the revenue to support it. Leverage, it turns out, works both ways.

All of these former robust sales activities, based on a tourist and entertainment model, have come to an abrupt halt with the arrival of Covid-19. It seems the time has come for Texas wineries to embrace technology and get fully onboard with online wine sales.

The first thing we need to consider in the Texas wine industry is that we don't know how long Covid-19 disruptions will continue. An August 4, 2020, edition of the *Atlantic* has an article by Sarah Zhang titled "The Coronavirus Is Never Going Away: No matter what happens now, the virus will continue to circulate around the world."[24] She writes:

"The coronavirus is simply too widespread and too transmissible. The most likely scenario, experts say, is that the pandemic ends at some point—because enough people have been either infected or vaccinated—but the virus continues to circulate in lower levels around the globe. Cases will wax and wane over time. Outbreaks will pop up here and there. Even when a much-anticipated vaccine arrives, it is likely to only suppress but never completely eradicate the virus. (For context, consider that vaccines exist for more than a dozen human viruses but only one, smallpox, has ever been eradicated from the planet, and that took 15 years of immense global coordination.) We will probably be living with this virus for the rest of our lives."

It will probably become like the seasonal flu, something unpleasant but something we will have to mitigate and take precautions against. Whether that will lead to further shutdowns of venues like wineries and wine festivals remains to be seen.

But whether or not the coronavirus persists and whether it existed or not, wineries would still have to be prepared to move a major part of their sales online. The catastrophic effects of the coronavirus only collapsed the time period in which this shift must take place. The momentum and the potential for wine sales are online.

---

24 https://www.theatlantic.com/author/sarah-zhang/

Mitigating Strategies – Wine Clubs
and Virtual Wine Tastings

One mitigating strategy offered by Texas wineries is virtual wine tastings, offered through Facebook and Twitter. The general format is for the winery to announce the tasting to an email list of its customers and True Believers. Interested consumers can order wine, generally three to six bottles or so, delivered to their door. A few days later, there is a Facebook Live virtual tasting, with expert participants from the winery—perhaps the owner, the winemaker, even a blogger or supplier or other wine knowledgeable guest to discuss the wines as they and the virtual guests, possibly in the hundreds, open, taste, appraise and comment on them. Not quite as picturesque as a visit to the winery, but really, an in-depth learning experience and comparison of the wine with the full attention of top winemakers and experts. It's a reasonable trade-off, particularly if you are a serious wine connoisseur, more interested in the wine itself than the entertainment ambiance and atmosphere, although there is a role for both. One best practice, in an approach to an online presence, is Becker Vineyards, which archives its tastings on its Facebook Page so continuously increases its online engagement.

Another online wine event is "Texas Wine Twitter Tuesdays." There's no registration or signup necessary. Log in to Twitter and follow the hashtag #txwine every Tuesday from 7 to 8 p.m. Instead of preordering a particular set of wines, this come-one-come-all initiative has a weekly calendar of styles and categories of wines, encouraging would-be participants to bring what they like to the tasting. (The topics in the first few weeks of May, for example, included Mother's Day wines, sparkling wines, Blanc du Bois, Lenoir and wine pairings for grilled food.) Though organizers lead the virtual conversation, anyone can chime in. Participants often include Texas winemakers and grape growers, along with sommeliers and Texas wine fans who share tasting notes, anecdotes, pairings and photos.

Another online event is one we strongly support. The Wonder Women of Wine (WWOW), an organization based out of Austin established in 2018 that advocates for Texas women in the wine industry and supports leadership positions for them, hosts Texas Tuesdays. This informative and fun broadcast series showcases Texas woman responsible for driving the Texas wine industry to new levels.

All of these wine events certainly increase the online presence of Texas wines and mitigate the lessened profitability or break-even challenge of Texas wines in the time of Covid-19. But none of them completely replace the necessity of moving online with a robust wine sales site, with the goal of not only satisfying the needs of existing wine clientele, but continuously educating people on wine taste and availability and recruiting new wine aficionados, bringing them into an efficient wine sales pipeline.

The Time to get online is now.

And it might be added that "he who hesitates (may well be) lost."

According to Forbes, "Internet shopping has grown more in the past 12 weeks than it did during the last decade."[25] That fact alone should settle the question of whether now is the time to get online with wine sales in a large scale, thoroughly professional way.

Nothing could be clearer than the imperative to get online with one's sales initiatives, bearing in mind that being an accomplished professional in the Texas wine industry is separate and distinct from being an accomplished technical, content marketing and social media professional online, one who is willing to devote the entire effort to Texas wine. An online marketplace gives winemakers the ability to reach customers where they live … which is increasingly on their mobile devices; to provide them with a pleasant and frictionless experience and to increase the winemaker's own productivity through automation and standard processes.

There are some Texas winemakers who appear to have met this imperative and dealt with it with great skill and grace. Becker Vineyards, William Chris Vineyards and Grape Creek Winery sell online through some of the biggest wine clubs. It may be that they had long had success in building up their email lists. And there may be other wineries who have been able to do the same. Texas has five or so very large and commercially successful wineries producing over 100,000 gallons of wine that may be able to sustain themselves in this extremely restricted environment. Texas has one winery , Mesa Vineyards/Ste. Genevieve, the behemoth associated with the powerful and deep-pocketed University of Texas, capable of producing over a million gallons of wine and it has very large, diverse and profitable contracts.

---

25 https://www.forbes.com/sites/stephenmcbride1/2020/07/24/shopify-is-seizing-an-80-billion-pot-of-gold/

Family-owned Messina Hoff, another giant in the Texas wine industry, already has locations in Bryan/College Station, Fredericksburg and Grapevine, Texas, and is constructing another with multiple hospitality venues in a planned community near Houston, a huge market. Llano Estacado Winery, Becker Vineyards, William Chris Vineyards and Duchman Family Winery are all large and may be well positioned to weather this challenging wine sales environment.

These wineries have the capability of hiring the best online technical support available, although some may not have sufficient technical background to sort out which capabilities and features might be best for their brand and their business model. Some Texas wineries, have fully embraced online technology so have not had to pare down staff and operations. Others, understandably, have not had the bandwidth to undertake a whole new sales model, particularly one that is tech heavy with many moving parts. These smaller wine growers may be able to host a website and post their wines for sale, but they do not have the expertise, professional tools, research or, generally, the in-depth capability to be constantly gathering traffic and updating their offering.

The Problem

So, the problem is actually twofold:

Wineries are dependent on retaining as much profit as possible from sales in their wine-tasting rooms, retail shelves and restaurants. However, with their limitation of distance and space and, in the time of Covid-19, the ability to stay open, they need the ability to sell more wine in a simple, customer-friendly, frictionless and inexpensive way.

Wine buyers, without the ability to visit wine-tasting rooms, which are spread out, or attend wine festivals, to actually taste various wines against each other, need a way to learn more about individual wines, read reviews and commentaries, or watch videos and continuously learn which wines are likely to appeal to them.

The Solution – Wine Sales Online

The solution is to build a website, with all the latest technology, tools and auto-mation, that will continue to educate, entertain and grow the Texas wine consumer community and provide a simple, inexpensive online sales platform for individual Texas wineries, should they choose to use it.

The Perfect Model – AdvancingTexasWine.com

As Covid-19 hit and spread in spring 2020, the deepening ramifications of its impact began to take hold for many of us. With a kind of horror, I realized the implications, not only to our lives, but to the livelihoods of many and to the industry I helped start and to which I felt deeply connected.

I could see clearly the hole that would be created and continuously deepen in the market. Wineries rely on sales from their wine-tasting rooms where they are allowed to keep all the profits. Retail and wholesale tiers take a big bite out of profits. Typically, restaurants and bars take around a 70% profit margin on wine. Retailers often make between 30% to 50%. Ouch! That's a lot of money going out the door, when, ideally, the winemaker could be retaining more. That profit structure provided winemakers a very good reason for expanding into the hospitality business, providing multiple spaces and venues for not only wine sales but rental and retail income. But the arrival of Covid-19 and the need for social distancing more or less exploded that business model, at least, in the best case scenario, temporarily. And one of the problems with online sales sites like Wine.com is that they are not building a proprietary identity for Texas wine. They are aggregating it with every other wine, and therefore, in my judgement, to some extent, treating it as a commodity. That's not a good thing.

I decided, with the help of tech teams and the collaboration of winery owners and the blessing of the TABC, to create the perfect business model to overcome this challenging time that had impacted us all. When contemplating putting in the work and investment needed to develop and build out this platform, I thought of Peter Sichel, former owner of Blue Nun winery. When tastes changed and sales of Blue Nun began to plummet, Peter sold his company in 1995 (although the wines have since rebounded, being vinified as a dryer and sometimes lively, sparkling wine for a more contemporary palette). But he was still deeply immersed in the wine business, traveling constantly and internationally to judge wine competitions and to consult.

Through collaborating with and advising colleagues and friends, Peter soon had an opportunity to buy into Château Fourcas Hosten, Listrac, on a riverbank, just miles from Margaux. Peter Sichel was in the game again. He saw an opportunity to jump back into a business he loved and he did so, with a very prestigious wine producing estate, with a chateau he and his family could stay in during their seasonal visits.

After leaving the business side of the Texas wine industry in the early eighties,

I always thought I might one day reenter the Texas wine scene, if I could do it in a way that made sense.

What makes sense to me now, is first, recording the history of the birth of the contemporary wine business, since much appears to remain unknown or shrouded in mystery for many, including many active in the wine industry. In my judgement, knowing the history, the science and the thought process always enriches one's understanding of an industry and enables better decision-making in the future. Then, equally important, I want to try to help assure the Texas wine industry survival through developing an online wine sales platform in this time of Covid-19. AdvancingTexasWine.com will be a wine sales platform open to all Texas wineries that wish to join us and use it to increase sales and continuous customer development.

The experience I bring to this endeavor includes having launched a website, AdvancingWomen.com, and marketing it successfully, amassing wide recognition for over 20 years in the media and the commercial and academic communities. With my background in agribusiness and the business basics of the Texas wine industry, combined with my experience in bringing a subject to a mass audience on the Net, I feel confident we can bring a valuable experience to wine lovers and explorers and provide an effective and efficient wine sales platform to those Texas vintners who want it and choose to be a part of this Texas project. What I envision is a complimentary period of several months after a winery registers to participate as a vendor in our multi-vendor wine marketplace, during which time we build out the site, scale the marketplace and develop traffic sufficient to sustain it at a profitable level for all. In the beginning, 100% of the sales price will go to the winery. At some point in the future, I will be happy to agree to any reasonable compensation, either in an instant split payment or my billing for marketing later. I am working with the TABC now in order to keep in strict compliance with their interpretation of any regulations affecting payment. My goal is to maintain a bright red line between marketing and all winery operations, including delivery.

There are many online tools at our disposal. One is automation of processes. Within that quiver is the ability to daily update wine news, trends and blogs, educating and updating consumers, giving them a reason to come back daily. Content marketing is powerful, and wine is an endlessly fascinating subject.

Back To My Roots and on to the Future

As I began to work to put together this website, I had to reach back in time, to some of my most talented tech colleagues and to vineyard and winery owners to hear their stories and find what they needed most.

One of the joys of the process was reconnecting with those vintners who have chosen Blue Mountain, near Fort Davis, as the home of their vineyards and the birthplace of their future wines. It is very heartening to learn many still consider that some of the best grapes in Texas come from this specific microclimate.

As I reached out to owners, I received a variety of responses.

Radiologist physician Jack Wright, in 2011, purchased 40 acres a half mile away from my old Blue Mountain Vineyard to create his new Blue Mountain Trail Vineyard. He went on to develop the Jack Rabbit Winery, and his wines are sold under the Château Wright label.

I emailed Jack in August to introduce myself and check on how things were going at his vineyard.

He responded by first saying: "I thought Gretchen Glasscock was dead." I assured him "News of my death has been greatly exaggerated." We had a pleasant conversation, but it was the middle of harvest for him so we didn't get too far beyond that.

Next I discovered online Alta Marfa, started by Ricky Taylor and now wife, Kate, who purchased three acres near Blue Mountain and rounded up 30 volunteers to help them plant 6,000 vines. They have lived in a tent that "has survived a fire, snow, brutal sun and lots and lots of wind." It has now been replaced with a bit more permanent A-frame they built themselves with the help of friends and volunteers. Ricky says in his blog: "It was a little sad to see it go, but I can't say I'm going to miss the icicles forming on my mustache in the middle of the night." In the midst of all this, Ricky and Kate went to Japan on their honeymoon.

He has his own solar irrigation system which, for a time, was controlled from his then-home in Houston. They have now made their first wine, a Tempranillo, at Robert Clay Vineyards and sold their first wine (Lazer Cat).

I have to say, I am a big fan of Ricky's blog. It is like I believe him to be, although I haven't yet met him in person: clever, smart, adventurous and bold.

Seeing what Ricky is able to create with the most fundamental of materials gives me great hope for the future of his vineyard and winery and the wine industry in Texas in general. Young people who "sail against the wind" and take on long odds are what every young industry needs to give it a shot of adrenaline and, just as important, hope that sustains it.

My heart really goes out to Dan and Maura Sharp who've taken on the challenge of cultivating the Vineyard at Blue Mountain, just where my vineyard once stood. At one point, very sadly, it was wiped out by disease, and several owners have dedicated themselves to reviving it. The Sharps define themselves as caretakers of a special place, and, of course, I believe they are, and are well suited for that honorable job.

Both Dan and Maura are pursuing certification in viticulture and the wine industry. I would like to tell you, in their own words, how they view their future at Blue Mountain.

"Our Plans"

"We do not view ourselves as owners of this special land as much as stewards of it for now—until it's time to pass it on to the next generation. We want to conserve and protect as much natural habitat on the ranch as possible. We plan to farm sustainably, which includes having an economically sustainable business. We also want to create opportunities for others in our community to learn about wine grape growing and how they can be part of the Texas wine industry.

"We are blessed that in addition to the humans and two vineyard dogs, a litany of wildlife calls our ranch home—mule deer, whitetail deer, Montezuma quail, blue quail, elk, mountain lions, javelina, aoudad, and a host of other birds, bees, bats and butterflies. This was their home long before it was ours.

"We will plant 1,500 new vines in April 2020 and plan to add another 4,500 in 2021. Eventually, we hope to have up to 20 acres of productive vines."

I applaud their efforts and have been in contact with the Sharps and find them extremely supportive of the Texas wine industry. As it turns out, they were very interested in learning about the original vineyard and the farming methods used. This information hadn't been recorded elsewhere and was lost in time. Fortunately, I had begun writing this book and was able to send them all the background and information about the choice of location and how the vineyard location came to be. We have vowed to be mutually supportive and whenever we get through the Covid-19 crisis, I hope to be able to give them a visit. They also have a wonderful blog and will be sharing some great and very encouraging photos of the progress at Blue Mountain, which I plan to attribute to them and share on our website.

It is really great, I believe, that blogging has become such a universal form of expression and so many people are so good at it. I think that must come from the artistic streak in wine making; as I have always said, wine is a fusion of art and agriculture.

So my very best to Dan and Maura Sharp and the vineyard we all love at Blue Mountain.

Closer to home, Texas Hills Vineyard, near Johnson City, is right down the road from Blanco, where the Glasscock family got its start. So naturally, it caught my interest. Of course, it is also in the heart of the Texas Hill Country wine scene.

"Located in the Texas Hill Country AVA, in the Pedernales River Valley where the soil is sandy loam over clay which is perfect for grape growing, Texas Hills Vineyard was planted in 1995. Kathy and Gary Gilstrap purchased the land just outside Johnson City because it reminded them of the Tuscan countryside they loved to visit. These Texas wine activists and pioneers of the Texas wine industry started both of the wine trails that put the Texas Hill Country to the forefront as a premium Texas wine region. From the granite countertops of their tasting room to their scored cement floors to their rammed earth walls, the tasting room has an inviting and comfortable feeling. Their award winning wines taste just as good at home, after delivery to your doorstep."

Kathy and Gary graciously agreed to work with me and AdvancingTexasWine.com to offer their wines and to be featured on our wine sales website so we could present a preview to other Texas wineries. This preview will give winery owners a password-protected section where they can review every aspect of the sales process, from start to finish, so they can decide for themselves whether they wish to register to work with us. If they do, they will select, list and price their own products, receive instant, direct payment and make their own delivery. Wine and control never leave their hands. What's not to like?

A Green Light for the Texas Wine Industry

For myself, I am reminded of F. Scott Fitzgerald's *The Great Gatsby* and the green light that burned, day and night, through the mist at the end of Gatsby's dock. It was an enchanted object that represented both a romantic past and dreams of a much sought-after future. I believe a wine website that we collaborate on and share, AdvancingTexasWine.com, can represent both of these, a rich past and a profitable and celebrated future. We can continue to add to it and shape it as our industry grows. It can have many directions and many layers, even as it fulfills its most basic job, of seeing us all through this difficult period.

We raise our glasses in a toast to all those in the Texas wine industry. Sustaining it through this perilous time is a big challenge. But we already have our chips on the table. And I believe we must seize the moment. I am all in, and I hope you will join me. I believe, with our love of the Texas wine industry and the long road we have traveled so far, our ultimate success is assured.

CHAPTER NINE

Afterword

I not only lived through this epic battle and historic victory, and the challenging times that led up to the development of the contemporary wine industry in Texas, but I have recollected and written that history, with the underpinning of extensive documentation, photos, contemporaneous articles and media that tell a much more complete and accurate story. I have donated all these materials to Texas Tech University, TTU at Fredericksburg, through Edward Hellman, Ph.D., Professor of Viticulture and Enology, with the shared hope of supporting and finding different paths forward for the growing multibillion-dollar Texas wine industry.

Photos

Gretchen Glasscock sharing wine comments with Peter Sichel, wine icon, celebrity and then President of Blue Nun Wines, largest selling wine in the world at that time.

Leon Adams, famed wine authority and scholar schools Gretchen in some of the finer points of the wine they are sharing.

Ely Callaway, wine pioneer of new climate region, Temecula, California and innovator, CEO of Callaway Golf, creator of "Big Bertha" golf clubs.

Certificate of Gretchen's induction into Knights of the Vine, prestigious wine brother and sisterhood of wine, dating back to the 13th century.

Glasscock was catching a Tejas Airlines flight to an industry event in Corpus, when she encountered their airline magazine. Ironically, the flight was overbooked, and the flight attendant leaned in and asked if anyone wanted to deplane and wait for a later flight. After a silence, she called Glasscock's name, but Glasscock tightened her seat belt and remained on the flight.

Glasscock, in her Broadway, San Antonio, Texas office, received media attention for her diligent search for the best climate conditions in Texas, and subsequent passage of the Farm Winery Act in 1979.

Tejas magazine gave her Blue Mountain Vineyard a big spread as Glasscock Wine Country.

Gretchen inspects some of her grapes at the Blue Mountain Vineyard.

After the passage of the Farm Winery Act, Glasscock's communication team presented her with a gavel, with a silver band engraved with "Gretchen's Wine Press," meant to acknowledge that together, they had not only pressed grapes, they had pressed the opposition to the mat and walked away victorious.

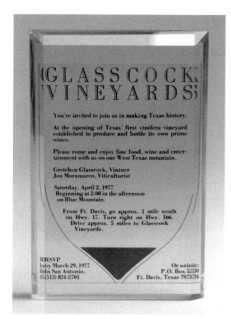

Glasscock Vineyard's invitation to our historic and festive opening ceremony for Texas first commercial vinifera vineyard at Blue Mountain in Jeff Davis County, West Texas. Celebrants included about 250 state officials, wine enthusiasts, Texas wine activists, university professors working on vineyard wine experimentation and local, as well as other Texas ranchers.

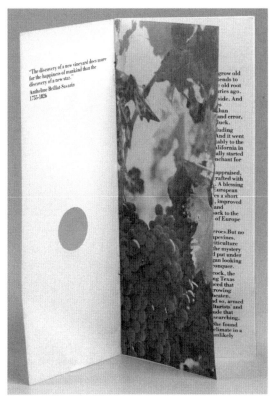

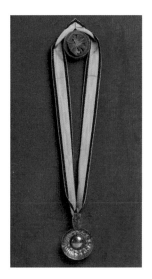

My communication team did a lot of educating various stakeholders about wine and, specifically, the potential for wine in Texas. This brochure started with "Sip the richness of our Texas sunsets. The clarity of our unspoiled sky. And the serenity of our blue mountain. " After a lot of factual info about our climate selection process, it ended with "Our Future is Rosé . And Burgundy. And So Forth."

Knights of the Vine wine tasting sash and cup, and cup deail.

Index

Made in the USA
Las Vegas, NV
21 January 2021